Fractions, Decimals and Percentages

Fractions 3

Teacher's Guide

Hilary Koll and Steve Mills

Schofield & Sims

Free downloads available from the Schofield & Sims website

A selection of free downloads is available from the Schofield & Sims website (www.schofieldandsims.co.uk/free-downloads). These may be used to further enhance the effectiveness of the programme. The downloads add to the range of print materials supplied in the teacher's guides.

- **Graphics** slides containing the visual elements from each teacher's guide unit provided as Microsoft PowerPoint® presentations.

- **Go deeper investigations** providing additional extension material to develop problem-solving and reasoning skills.

- **Additional resources** including a fraction wall, a comparison chart and number lines to support learning and teaching.

Published by **Schofield & Sims Ltd**, Dogley Mill, Fenay Bridge, Huddersfield HD8 0NQ, UK
Telephone 01484 607080
www.schofieldandsims.co.uk

This edition copyright © Schofield & Sims Ltd, 2017
First published in 2017

Authors: **Hilary Koll and Steve Mills**
Hilary Koll and Steve Mills have asserted their moral rights under the Copyright, Designs and Patents Act, 1988, to be identified as the authors of this work.

British Library Cataloguing in Publication Data
A catalogue record for this book is available from the British Library.

Design by **Oxford Designers & Illustrators Ltd**
Printed in the UK by **Page Bros (Norwich) Ltd**

ISBN 978 07217 1380 9

Contents

Overview

Fractions, decimals and percentages are frequent areas of difficulty in mathematics for primary school pupils. Many teachers find them challenging to teach and pupils often have limited or only partially developed conceptual understanding of the topics. A major reason children struggle with fractions, decimals and percentages is the variety of contexts and representations in which they appear – for example, as areas, as sets, on number lines, as a result of a division problem and in relation to measurements.

Schofield & Sims Fractions, Decimals and Percentages is a structured whole-school programme designed to help pupils develop a deep, secure and adaptable understanding of these topics. The series consists of six pupil books and six teacher's guides, one for each primary school year.

Each unit of the programme addresses a single learning objective. The teacher's guides provide detailed teaching notes with accompanying graphics to use in lessons. The pupil books provide a summary of the learning objective and a set of related practice questions that increase in difficulty. This allows you, the teacher or adult helper, to introduce and teach a particular concept and then to provide appropriate intelligent practice which gradually leads children towards more complex representations and varied contexts.

Supporting a mastery approach, all pupils are encouraged to move at the same pace through the units and are given the same opportunity to fully understand the concept being taught. Depth of learning is emphasised over speed of learning and the pupils should have a solid understanding of the content of each unit before moving on to new material. Downloadable **Go deeper** extension resources help to cement pupils' understanding of the concepts that have been taught. The series also provides ongoing and integrated assessment throughout.

Fractions 3 and the National Curriculum

Fractions 3 and its related **Teacher's Guide** match the statutory requirements for Year 3 for 'Fractions' in the National Curriculum. The seven statutory requirements are listed below. They have been coded for ease of reference. For example, Y3/F1 refers to the first fractions requirement in Year 3.

National Curriculum requirements for 'Fractions'

Y3/F1 Count up and down in tenths; recognise that tenths arise from dividing an object into 10 equal parts and in dividing one-digit numbers or quantities by 10.

Y3/F2 Recognise, find and write fractions of a discrete set of objects: unit fractions and non-unit fractions with small denominators.

Y3/F3 Recognise and use fractions as numbers: unit fractions and non-unit fractions with small denominators.

Y3/F4 Recognise and show, using diagrams, equivalent fractions with small denominators.

Y3/F5 Add and subtract fractions with the same denominator within one whole (for example, $\frac{5}{7} + \frac{1}{7} = \frac{6}{7}$).

Y3/F6 Compare and order unit fractions, and fractions with the same denominators.

Y3/F7 Solve problems that involve all of the above.

National Curriculum coverage chart

This chart maps all the units and tests in **Fractions 3** against the National Curriculum requirements. When reading the chart, please refer to the curriculum coding introduced on page 4. The light shaded boxes show where a requirement is touched upon and the dark shaded boxes show the key units and tests for that requirement.

Legend: ■ = dark shaded (key unit/test) · ░ = light shaded (touched upon) · blank = not covered

	Y2 Revision	Y3/F1	Y3/F2	Y3/F3	Y3/F4	Y3/F5	Y3/F6	Y3/F7
Unit 1	■				░	░		■
Unit 2	■		■		░	░		░
Unit 3				■	░		■	░
Unit 4			░	■			░	■
Unit 5			░	░			■	░
Unit 6				■				■
Check-up test 1			░	■				■
Unit 7				■	░	░		■
Unit 8		■		░	░		■	░
Unit 9		░		■			■	░
Unit 10		░		■	░	░	■	░
Unit 11		░		░			■	■
Unit 12			■	░		░		■
Check-up test 2		■	■	■	░	░	■	■
Unit 13		░	■		░	░	░	■
Unit 14		░			■		░	■
Unit 15		░	░		■		░	■
Unit 16		░		■	░	■	░	░
Unit 17		░		■		■	░	░
Unit 18		░	░		░	░	░	░
Check-up test 3		■	■	■	■	■	■	■
Final test		■	■	■	■	■	■	■

Prerequisites for Fractions 3

Before beginning **Fractions 3** the pupils should have an understanding of halves and quarters. Each year of the programme, however, begins with some revision to ensure that the pupils understand the necessary ideas to move forward. The first column in the National Curriculum coverage chart on page 5, labelled 'Y2 Revision', shows the units that revise Year 2 material. The pupils can be given **Fractions 2** first if they require further practice to build their confidence and understanding.

The focus in Year 3 is on the following areas: counting in tenths, dividing one-digit numbers by 10, fractions of sets, unit fractions, equivalent fractions with small denominators, adding and subtracting fractions with the same denominator, comparing and ordering fractions, and problem solving.

Fractions 3 Teacher's Guide

The **Fractions 3 Teacher's Guide** contains everything you need to teach the National Curriculum requirements for 'Fractions' in Year 3. There are 18 corresponding units in the teacher's guide and pupil book, six for each term.

Using the Teacher's notes

In this teacher's guide you will find **Teacher's notes** for each unit (pages 12 to 47). These include a detailed lesson plan with accompanying graphics that can be used to demonstrate the learning objective before the pupils begin the activities in the pupil book. The graphics are visual prompts for the class and can be used in a variety of ways. They are all available as interactive PowerPoint® presentations (free to download from the Schofield & Sims website). Alternatively, the graphics could be presented on a projector, or photocopied and used as pupil handouts, or used as a guide when drawing your own visual prompts. The lesson plans can be easily adapted to suit your classroom. Below is an example lesson from this teacher's guide, alongside the corresponding slides from the **Fractions 3** Powerpoint® presentation.

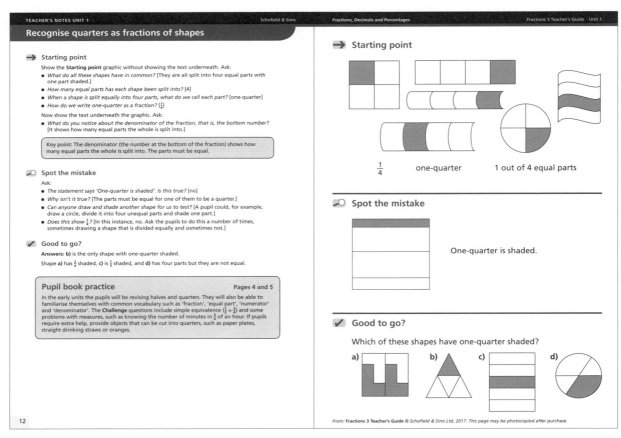

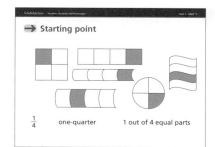  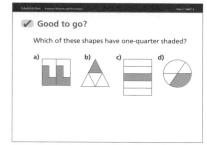

The **Teacher's notes** for each unit are divided into the following sections:

- **Starting point** – This section provides clear instruction on how to introduce and teach the learning objective. Using the graphics as prompts, probing questions are given that draw on the pupils' prior knowledge and encourage them to find connections, reason and reach conclusions about why the concept being taught is true. The **Key point** of the lesson is clearly highlighted.

- **Spot the mistake** – This is a statement, often with a visual element, that represents a mistake which is commonly made with the concept being taught. The statement is intentionally incorrect. You are given a series of corrective questions to ask the pupils, drawing out potential misconceptions and helping them to spot the mistake. Procedural understanding is deepened as the pupils discuss why the statement is incorrect and what the correct statement should be.

- **Good to go?** – This section has quick practice questions that help you establish whether each pupil has understood the lesson and is a useful tool for formative assessment. It is suggested that the pupils answer these questions on mini-whiteboards and hold up their answers. This helps you to quickly identify the pupils who require further assistance and those who have fully understood the unit focus.

- **Pupil book practice** – This section provides links to the pupil book pages for this unit. It flags potential areas of difficulty to be aware of in the activities, highlights when questions act as a bridge to later units, and offers further suggestions for practical resources you can use to support the pupils as they work.

Answers

The teacher's guide contains a complete set of **Answers** (pages 48 to 93) for all the units and tests in the pupil book. The answers are presented as correctly completed pupil book pages to make marking quick and easy.

Fractions 3 Pupil Book

Once you are confident that the pupils have grasped the concept of the lesson, they should turn to the corresponding unit in their pupil book. This offers varied activities of increasing difficulty that provide plenty of repetition, practice and challenge to consolidate learning.

The pupil book begins with a simple introduction which clearly explains the purpose of the book and how it is used. This introduction supports your own instructions for the pupils as they start this book. It is also a useful reference for parents if you decide to set sections of the pupil book as homework. On the following page is an example lesson from the pupil book.

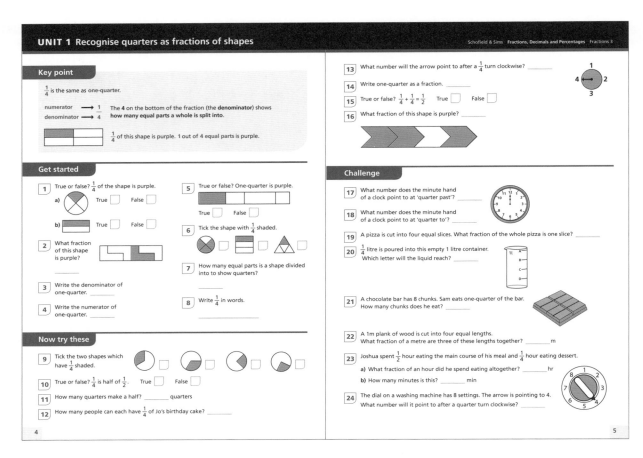

Each unit in the pupil book begins with a child-friendly summary of the **Key point** of the lesson, as a reminder for the pupil and to assist parents in supporting their children at home.

The practice questions in each unit are divided into three sections.

- **Get started** – Quick questions to help the pupil gain confidence in the topic, with a variety of straightforward practice questions related to the learning objective.

- **Now try these** – Additional number and practical problems to take the topic further with more varied vocabulary and representations.

- **Challenge** – Problem-solving questions involving greater challenge, such as measurement and money contexts and links to other more complex concepts.

The pupils should write their answers directly into their own pupil book. Each completed pupil book provides a permanent record of achievement and encourages the pupils to take pride in their work. Three **Check-up tests**, one for the end of each term, a **Final test** and a **How did I find it?** checklist are also included in each pupil book. These help you to monitor the pupils' progress.

Strategies for learning

If a pupil is struggling with a question, prompt them to try it again using a different strategy. Problem-solving strategies develop deeper mathematical thinking, allowing pupils to solve a wider variety of problems.

- **Visualising** – *Sketch a picture of the situation or use real-life objects to model it.*

- **Simplifying** – *If a problem seems too difficult, make it easier. For example, change decimals into whole numbers, and work out how you would solve the easier problem. Then go back to the harder problem and see if you can find the answer.*

- **Using trial and improvement** – *It can help to guess what the answer might be. Look at the question again, with the guessed number in mind, and see how your guess needs to be changed. Sometimes you can get an idea of whether the answer is larger or smaller than your guess. Choose an adjusted number and keep repeating this until you get to the right answer.*

- **Reasoning** – *Discuss the problem with a partner and make suggestions such as 'If you tried adding, would that work?' or 'Do you think dividing would give us the answer?'. Suggestions don't have to be right but they can really help to get you thinking.*

- **Looking for patterns** – *Look out for patterns in the numbers in a problem. Sometimes you can find an answer by spotting a pattern and continuing it.*

- **Generalising** – *Some problems involve thinking of an idea more generally or saying whether a statement is never, sometimes or always true. For this you must generalise. This means thinking carefully about an idea in lots of different situations.*

- **Checking** – *Go back and check your answers. You could use inverse operations or work backwards from the answer. Make sure you haven't made any wrong assumptions.*

- **Persevering** – *When all else fails, keep going! Try using a coloured pen to highlight the important numbers in the problem and see if that helps you to spot a pattern.*

Go deeper

When teaching for mastery, differentiation is achieved by emphasising depth of knowledge and mathematical fluency over pace of learning. The **Challenge** questions in the pupil book offer sophisticated problems that will stretch even the more able student and provide the practice that is required to exceed the expected national standards. **Go deeper investigations** are also available (free to download from the Schofield & Sims website), which correspond with the content covered up to each **Check-up test**. These group work problem-solving activities help pupils to delve more deeply into the concepts being taught and cement their understanding. Teacher's notes and pupil worksheets are provided for each investigation. These can be used with the whole class in a dedicated problem-solving lesson or as extension material for pupils who require further challenge.

Assessment

Fractions 3 and its related **Teacher's Guide** offer frequent opportunities and multiple resources for in-school assessment. These resources should be used in line with your school's own assessment policy.

Formative assessment

The teacher's guide lesson plans all feature precise questioning. This can be used as part of your ongoing formative assessment to test the pupils' conceptual and procedural knowledge. The questions can help to uncover a pupil's reasoning and depth of mathematical thinking. The **Good to go?** section at the end of each lesson provides a further check, enabling you to easily identify when pupils are struggling and when they are ready to progress to the pupil book practice questions.

The pupil book units can also be used as a basis for formative assessment. Teachers should monitor the progress that each pupil is making as they work through the pupil book questions. If an answer is incorrect, asking the pupil to explain how they reached this answer may reveal gaps in understanding that can then be addressed.

Three **Check-up tests** are provided in the pupil book. These can be used to test pupils' understanding of the material covered in the preceding six units. This allows you to ascertain how well the pupils have remembered the ideas covered in the programme so far and how secure their understanding is.

Each pupil's day-to-day progress can be monitored by using the **Pupil progress chart** (at the back of this book). This chart can be photocopied for each pupil in your class so that you can keep track of the marks scored on each unit and **Check-up test**. Guidance is provided below on how to interpret the information gained from the **Pupil progress chart**.

Decoding the unit scores

While the total score achieved in each pupil book unit will be a good indicator of the pupils' overall progress, it is advisable to keep an eye out for patterns in their scores across the three different sections as well.

- If a pupil struggles with **Get started**, it can indicate that the pupil has not yet understood or has misunderstood the concept of the unit and is likely to require further support.

- If a pupil struggles with **Now try these** after a successful **Get started**, it can indicate that the pupil has understood the initial idea but is having trouble applying it to different contexts and with different representations.

- If a pupil struggles with **Challenge** after a successful **Get started** and **Now try these**, it can indicate that the pupil may need further help in problem-solving processes such as reasoning, simplifying, visualising, looking for patterns or generalising. It may also indicate that the pupil is having difficulty with comprehension skills, misunderstanding the language that is used in the question.

- If the pupil is able to make a good attempt at **Challenge** after a successful **Get started** and **Now try these**, it can indicate that the pupil has mastered the unit and is secure in their understanding of the concepts that have been taught.

- If the pupil scores highly across all three sections, it can indicate that the pupil has mastered the concepts of the unit at greater depth.

- Look out for inconsistent scoring across the sections, for example, a low score in **Get started** and a high score in **Now try these** or a low score in **Now try these** and a high score in **Challenge** as this may mean that there are gaps in the pupil's understanding. Some guesswork may have been involved in gaining correct answers.

> ### Decoding the Check-up test scores
>
> - A score of 0–14 can indicate that the pupil has not yet understood all of the key concepts in the preceding units. Further consolidation work or a different approach may be needed to ensure secure understanding.
>
> - A score of 15–20 can indicate that the pupil has mastered the concepts of the preceding units and can confidently move forward.

Each pupil book also contains a **How did I find it?** checklist which enables the pupils to evaluate their own progress as they work through the programme. Each unit has a corresponding 'I can' statement. After completing each unit, **Check-up test** and **Final test** the pupils should be given the opportunity to rate how they found the unit – 'difficult', 'getting there' or 'easy'.

Summative assessment

The **Final test** in the pupil book can be used for in-school summative assessment at the end of **Fractions 3**. This test allows you to assess the pupils' understanding of all the concepts covered in **Fractions 3**. The **Final test** is organised so that each section tests a different statutory requirement for the Year 3 National Curriculum.

Marks for the **Final test** can be recorded on the **Final test group record sheet** (at the back of this book). Record each mark by either ticking or shading the relevant boxes next to each pupil's name. This chart outlines which curriculum requirement is being tested in each section using the curriculum coding that was introduced on page 4. It provides an at-a-glance overview of how the whole class is performing in relation to the National Curriculum requirements and enables you to evaluate pupil learning at the end of the year. Guidance is provided below on how to interpret the information gained from this chart.

> ### Decoding the Final test scores
>
> - A score of 0–20 marks can indicate that the pupil has not fully mastered the key concepts for the year. The curriculum coding should provide a clear idea of which requirements the pupil is struggling with. Catch-up work is likely to be needed in these areas before the pupil is ready to proceed with Year 4 material.
>
> - A score of 21–28 marks can indicate that the pupil has mastered the key concepts for the year and can confidently move forward to Year 4 material. The curriculum coding should provide a clear idea of the pupil's strengths and warn of any areas of weakness that may require additional practice in Year 4.

The **Final test group record sheet** provides a useful record for school leaders and inspectors and will show the subsequent teacher how secure each pupil was in their knowledge of the previous year's curriculum and how ready they are for progression.

Recognise quarters as fractions of shapes

➡ Starting point

Show the **Starting point** graphic without showing the text underneath. Ask:

- *What do all these shapes have in common?* [They are all split into four equal parts with one part shaded.]
- *How many equal parts has each shape been split into?* [4]
- *When a shape is split equally into four parts, what do we call each part?* [one-quarter]
- *How do we write one-quarter as a fraction?* [$\frac{1}{4}$]

Now show the text underneath the graphic. Ask:

- *What do you notice about the denominator of the fraction, that is, the bottom number?* [It shows how many equal parts the whole is split into.]

> **Key point:** The denominator (the number at the bottom of the fraction) shows how many equal parts the whole is split into. The parts must be equal.

🔎 Spot the mistake

Ask:

- *The statement says 'One-quarter is shaded'. Is this true?* [no]
- *Why isn't it true?* [The parts must be equal for one of them to be a quarter.]
- *Can anyone draw and shade another shape for us to test?* [A pupil could, for example, draw a circle, divide it into four unequal parts and shade one part.]
- *Does this show $\frac{1}{4}$?* [In this instance, no. Ask the pupils to do this a number of times, sometimes drawing a shape that is divided equally and sometimes not.]

✔ Good to go?

Answers: b) is the only shape with one-quarter shaded.

Shape **a)** has $\frac{2}{4}$ shaded, **c)** is $\frac{1}{5}$ shaded, and **d)** has four parts but they are not equal.

> # Pupil book practice   Pages 4 and 5
>
> In the early units the pupils will be revising halves and quarters. They will also be able to familiarise themselves with common vocabulary such as 'fraction', 'equal part', 'numerator' and 'denominator'. The **Challenge** questions include simple equivalence ($\frac{1}{2} = \frac{2}{4}$) and some problems with measures, such as knowing the number of minutes in $\frac{3}{4}$ of an hour. If pupils require extra help, provide objects that can be cut into quarters, such as paper plates, straight drinking straws or oranges.

Starting point

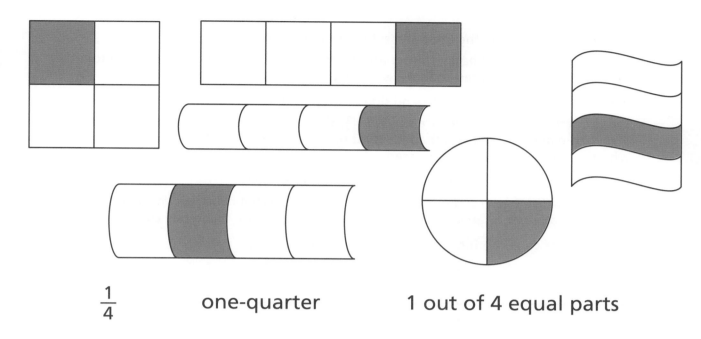

$$\frac{1}{4}$$ one-quarter   1 out of 4 equal parts

 ## Spot the mistake

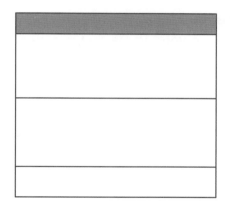

One-quarter is shaded.

 ## Good to go?

Which of these shapes have one-quarter shaded?

a) 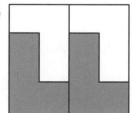   b) 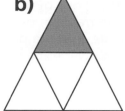   c) 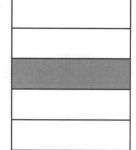   d)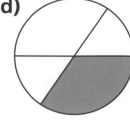

Recognise halves and quarters of sets

➡ Starting point

Show the set of cubes on the left-hand side of graphic **A**. Ask:

- *What fraction of the cubes in this set are shaded?* [$\frac{2}{4}$ or $\frac{1}{2}$] Show the cubes joined together, after the arrow, and reiterate that $\frac{1}{2}$ is shaded.

Show the set of cubes on the left-hand side of graphic **B**. Ask:

- *What fraction of these cubes are shaded?* [$\frac{1}{4}$] Show the cubes joined together, after the arrow, to emphasise that $\frac{1}{4}$ is shaded. Point out that the cubes will show the same fraction whether they are joined or separated.

Show the set of cubes on the left-hand side of graphic **C**. Say:

- *It is more difficult here to see what fraction is shaded. What could we do to help?* [Join the cubes together or arrange them in equal groups.] Reveal the joined cubes to show $\frac{1}{2}$.

Show the set of cubes on the left-hand side of graphic **D**. Ask:

- *What fraction of these cubes are shaded? How could we find out?* [Group them to show that $\frac{3}{4}$ are shaded.] Reveal the joined cubes to show $\frac{3}{4}$.

> **Key point:** Arrange items in equal groups to make it easier to find halves and quarters of sets of objects.

🔍 Spot the mistake

Ask:

- *The statement says 'One-half of the cards are shaded'. Is this true?* [no]
- *Why isn't it true?* [If the cards are arranged in two equal groups, you can see that less than half of the cards are shaded.]
- *Can we group them to find the correct answer?* [The cards can be arranged in four equal groups to show that $\frac{1}{4}$ of the cards are shaded.]
- *What fraction of the set is not shaded?* [$\frac{3}{4}$]

✔ Good to go?

Answers: a) $\frac{3}{4}$ **b)** $\frac{1}{4}$ **c)** $\frac{2}{4}$

The pupils may give the answer $\frac{2}{8}$ for **b)** or $\frac{4}{8}$ or $\frac{1}{2}$ for **c)**. These are also correct, though the pupils are not expected to give these answers at this stage.

A further question could be asked: *What fraction of each set is not shaded?* [a) $\frac{1}{4}$, b) $\frac{3}{4}$ or $\frac{6}{8}$, c) $\frac{2}{4}$, $\frac{4}{8}$ or $\frac{1}{2}$]

> ### Pupil book practice   **Pages 6 and 7**
>
> If pupils struggle with this concept, provide them with cubes to join together or to arrange into equal groups to help them decide whether $\frac{1}{4}$, $\frac{1}{2}$ or $\frac{3}{4}$ of the objects are being described. Note that, if the pupils have already encountered fractions other than halves and quarters, some of their answers may involve larger numbers, for example, $\frac{2}{8}$ rather than $\frac{1}{4}$. Accept these answers but encourage the pupils to also answer using halves and quarters.

➡️ Starting point

A

B

C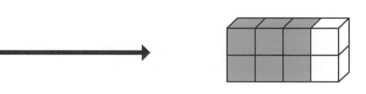

D

🔍 Spot the mistake

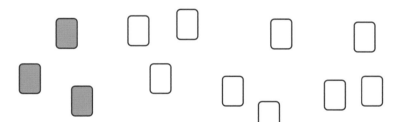

One-half of the
cards are shaded.

✔️ Good to go?

What fraction of each set of cards is shaded?

a)    b) 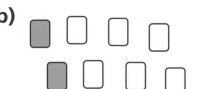   c)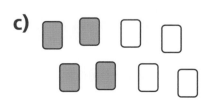

Count up and down in halves and quarters

→ Starting point

Display graphic **A** without showing the fraction notation underneath the number line. Ask:

- *Can you point to the first frog?* [The pupils point to the frog.] *How could you describe where on the number line this frog is?* Help the pupils to see that the frog is on the line halfway between 0 and 1. Establish that this can be written as $\frac{1}{2}$.

- *Where is the next frog?* [The pupils point to the frog.] *How could we use numbers to describe where it is?* Explain that a whole number and a fraction are used because the frog has hopped half more than 3 [$3\frac{1}{2}$]. Repeat to identify the last frog's position. [$7\frac{1}{2}$]

Reveal the fraction notation under the number line. Ask:

- *Let's imagine a frog hops along this number line in halves. Can you say each number with me?* Count on in halves together from 0 to 8. Then count back in halves from 8 to 0.

Display graphic **B** without showing the fraction notation underneath the number line. Explain that the line shows quarters. Count on and back in quarters together. Now reveal the fraction notation. Ask:

- *Can you see a frog at $2\frac{1}{2}$?* [yes]
- *We called this point $2\frac{2}{4}$ before. Can it have more than one name?* Discuss that $\frac{2}{4}$ can also be described as $\frac{1}{2}$.

You may want to introduce the term 'mixed number' at this point, or you may prefer to wait until Unit 8, when mixed numbers will be explored in more detail.

> **Key point:** To count on and back in halves and quarters. To use a whole number and fraction (mixed number) to identify points greater than one whole.

🔍 Spot the mistake

Ask:

- *The statement says 'The frog is on $\frac{3}{4}$'. Is this true?* [no]
- *Why isn't it true?* [The frog is on a number larger than 1.]
- *What is the correct answer?* [one and three-quarters]
- *How do we write that?* [$1\frac{3}{4}$]

✔ Good to go?

Answers: a) 2   **b)** 3   **c)** $1\frac{2}{4}$

The pupils may give the answer $1\frac{1}{2}$ for **c)**, which is also correct.

For extension, the pupils could be asked to give the next two numbers in each sequence, or they could look at sequences that include larger numbers.

Pupil book practice   Pages 8 and 9

Here the pupils are provided with the opportunity to use mixed numbers involving halves and quarters to solve related problems, including continuing sequences. If possible, give number lines showing halves and quarters to pupils who might struggle so that they can use them to count forwards and backwards. The **Challenge** questions include problems involving units of measurement such as litres, metres and kilograms and require the pupils to appreciate that $\frac{2}{4}$ is equal to $\frac{1}{2}$.

Starting point

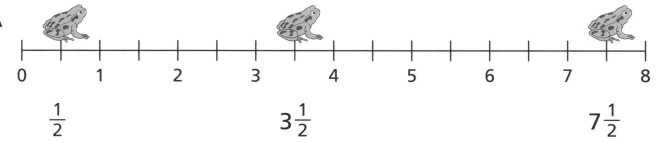

A

$\frac{1}{2}$ $3\frac{1}{2}$ $7\frac{1}{2}$

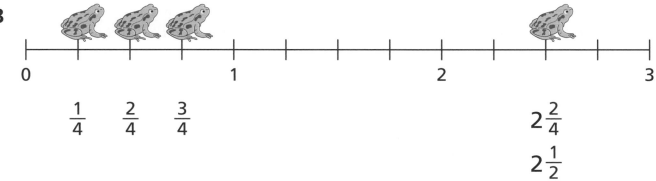

B

$\frac{1}{4}$ $\frac{2}{4}$ $\frac{3}{4}$ $2\frac{2}{4}$

$2\frac{1}{2}$

Spot the mistake

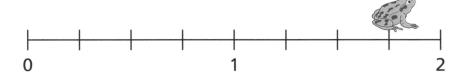

The frog is on $\frac{3}{4}$.

Good to go?

What number comes next?

a) 0, $\frac{1}{2}$, 1, $1\frac{1}{2}$, ▢

b) $2\frac{1}{4}$, $2\frac{2}{4}$, $2\frac{3}{4}$, ▢

c) $2\frac{1}{4}$, 2, $1\frac{3}{4}$, ▢

Understand fractions with the numerator 1

➡ Starting point

Show the **Starting point** graphic without the fraction notation underneath. Ask:

- *Which of these shapes has $\frac{1}{4}$ shaded?* [the middle shape]
- *How do you know?* [It is divided into four equal parts and one of the parts is shaded. None of the other shapes is divided into four equal parts.] Encourage the pupils to use the notation $\frac{1}{4}$ and describe it as one out of four equal parts.
- *How many equal parts has each of the other shapes been split into?* [6, 3, 5, 3, 8]
- *What fraction of the other shapes is shaded? How do we write each of these as a fraction?* [$\frac{1}{6}$, $\frac{1}{3}$, $\frac{1}{5}$, $\frac{1}{3}$, $\frac{1}{8}$]

Reveal the fraction notation and discuss which fraction applies to which shape.

- *What do you notice about the denominator, that is, the bottom number?* [It shows how many equal parts a whole is split into.] Watch out for pupils who incorrectly give the denominator as the number of unshaded parts, rather than the total number of parts including the shaded part.

> **Key point:** The denominator (the bottom number) shows how many equal parts a whole is split into. If the numerator (the top number) of a fraction is 1, the fraction is describing one part of the whole.

🔍 Spot the mistake

Ask:

- *The statement says '$\frac{1}{3}$ is shaded'. Is this true?* [no]
- *Why isn't it true?* [The shape must be divided into three equal parts for one of them to be a third.]
- *Can anyone use 3 cubes to make a shape where $\frac{1}{3}$ is a different colour?*
- *How do we know that $\frac{1}{3}$ of this shape is a different colour?* [All three parts of the shape are equal in size.]

✔ Good to go?

Answers: a) $\frac{1}{6}$ b) $\frac{1}{5}$ c) $\frac{1}{3}$ d) $\frac{1}{8}$

> ## Pupil book practice   Pages 10 and 11
>
> The **Get started** section consolidates the idea of splitting a whole shape into equal parts and identifying the name given to one of those parts. Later sections involve unit fractions in other representations, including one out of a number of objects in a set, and unit fractions of a metre or an hour and so on. The **Challenge** questions also include some references to non-unit fractions to extend higher achievers. Question 23 explores the idea of a unit fraction resulting from dividing 1 by a number, for example, $1 \div 3 = \frac{1}{3}$.

Starting point

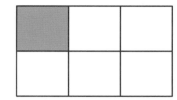
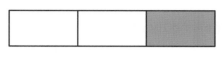
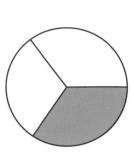
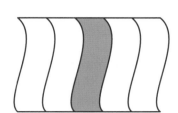

$$\frac{1}{4} \qquad \frac{1}{6} \qquad \frac{1}{3} \qquad \frac{1}{5} \qquad \frac{1}{8}$$

 ## Spot the mistake

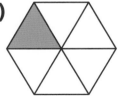 　　　$\frac{1}{3}$ is shaded.

 ## Good to go?

What fraction of each shape is shaded?

a) 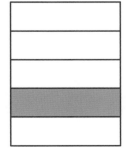　　b) 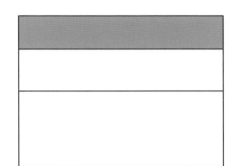　　c) 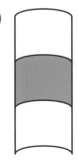　　d)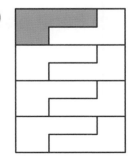

Compare fractions with the numerator 1

➡️ Starting point

Show graphic **A** without showing the fraction notation underneath. Ask:

- *How many equal parts has each circle been split into?* [3, 4, 5, 6, 8]
- *What fraction of each circle is shaded?* Establish the fraction shaded on each shape and reveal the notation. Explain that fractions with the numerator 1 are called 'unit fractions'.
- *Imagine each circle is a pizza, divided into equal parts as shown. If you could have only 1 slice of pizza and you were very hungry, which pizza would you choose to have a slice of?* [the first pizza]
- *Which fraction is the largest?* [$\frac{1}{3}$] *Which fraction is the smallest?* [$\frac{1}{8}$]
- *What do you notice about the denominator of the largest fraction?* [It is the smallest number.] *What do you notice about the denominator of the smallest fraction?* [It is the largest number.] Discuss this with the pupils. Establish that the more parts a whole is split into, the smaller each part will be. This means that the larger the denominator, the smaller each part will be.

Show the two statements in graphic **B**. Ask the pupils if the statements are true or false. [Both are true.] Use the circles in graphic **A** to check.

> **Key point:** When a whole is split into equal parts, the larger the denominator (the bottom number) of the unit fraction, the smaller each part will be.

🔍 Spot the mistake

Remind the pupils of the meaning of the greater and less than signs (< >). Ask:

- *The statement says '$\frac{1}{6} > \frac{1}{3}$'. Is this true?* [no]
- *Why isn't it true?* [The more parts a whole is split into, the smaller each part will be. As such, $\frac{1}{6}$ is less than $\frac{1}{3}$.]
- *Can anyone make up a new statement using the greater than or less than signs that we can test?* [Example: $\frac{1}{4} < \frac{1}{3}$]
- *What is it important to remember about the relationship between the size of the fractions and their denominators?* [The larger the denominator of a unit fraction, the smaller each part will be.]

✔️ Good to go?

Answers: a) $\frac{1}{3}$ **b)** $\frac{1}{4}$ **c)** $\frac{1}{5}$

Once the pupils have identified the larger fraction in each pair you could ask them which sign < or > should go between each pair. [**a)** >, **b)** >, **c)** <]

> ## Pupil book practice   **Pages 12 and 13**
>
> Pupils often find it hard to accept that fractions written with larger numbers may be smaller than those written with smaller numbers. The questions in the pupil book start with familiar fractions such as $\frac{1}{2}$ and $\frac{1}{4}$ and then extend to include a wider range of fractions to consolidate the idea more abstractly. Provide fraction diagrams for the pupils to refer to (such as those in the graphics) to allow them to check when unsure.

Starting point

A

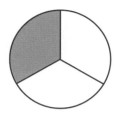 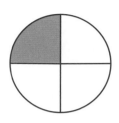 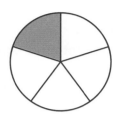 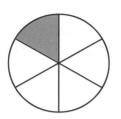 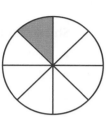

$\frac{1}{3}$ $\frac{1}{4}$ $\frac{1}{5}$ $\frac{1}{6}$ $\frac{1}{8}$

B $\frac{1}{3}$ is larger than $\frac{1}{4}$. $\frac{1}{8}$ is smaller than $\frac{1}{5}$.

 Spot the mistake

$\frac{1}{6} > \frac{1}{3}$

 Good to go?

Which fraction is larger in each pair?

a) $\frac{1}{3}$ $\frac{1}{5}$

b) $\frac{1}{4}$ $\frac{1}{8}$

c) $\frac{1}{6}$ $\frac{1}{5}$

Recognise unit fractions as a division of a quantity

➡️ **Starting point**

Show the first two rows in graphic **A**. Ask:

- *How can we find $\frac{1}{5}$ of £20?* [divide £20 into five equal parts]
- *Which number do we divide?* [the quantity, £20]
- *Which number do we divide by?* [the denominator or bottom number, 5]
- *Which related times tables fact can we use to help us find the answer?* [5 × 4 = 20 or 4 × 5 = 20]
- *What is $\frac{1}{5}$ of £20?* [£4] Reveal the bottom row of graphic **A** to confirm this.

Show graphic **B**. Ask:

- *How many equal parts has this number line been split into?* [8]
- *What length does the whole line represent?* [24cm]
- *How can we find $\frac{1}{8}$ of 24cm?* [divide 24cm into 8 equal parts]
- *Which number do we divide?* [the quantity, 24cm]
- *Which number do we divide by?* [the denominator, 8]
- *Which related times tables fact can we use to help us find the answer?* [3 × 8 = 24 or 8 × 3 = 24]
- *What is $\frac{1}{8}$ of 24cm?* [3cm]

> **Key point:** To find a unit fraction of a quantity, divide the quantity by the denominator.

🔍 **Spot the mistake**

Ask:

- *The statement says '$\frac{1}{5}$ of 10 = 50'. Is this true?* [no]
- *What is the mistake?* [The quantity was multiplied by the denominator rather than divided by it.]
- *How can we make the statement true?* [$\frac{1}{5}$ of 10 = 2 or $\frac{1}{5}$ of 250 = 50]

✔️ **Good to go?**

Answers: a) 9p   **b)** £7   **c)** 2m

Some pupils might find it useful to rewrite each question using a division sign before answering the questions, for example, $\frac{1}{3}$ of 27 = 27 ÷ 3.

Pupil book practice   Pages 14 and 15

The practice here focuses on finding unit fractions of numbers and measures. The **Challenge** questions require knowledge of the relationships between some units of measurement, such as 1 metre = 100 centimetres, and time, such as 60 minutes = 1 hour. In question 18, pupils will also need to know how to find the perimeter of a rectangle by finding the total length around the shape.

Starting point

A

$$£20$$

$\frac{1}{5}$ of £20 = £20 ÷ 5 = £ ◻

| £4 | £4 | £4 | £4 | £4 |

B

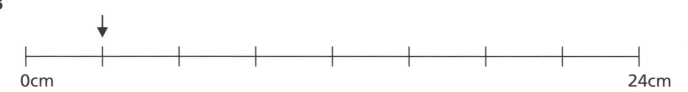

0cm   24cm

$\frac{1}{8}$ of 24cm = ◻ cm

Spot the mistake

$\frac{1}{5}$ of 10 = 50

Good to go?

a) Find $\frac{1}{3}$ of 27p.

b) Find $\frac{1}{4}$ of £28.

c) Find $\frac{1}{8}$ of 16m.

Understand non-unit fractions as areas of shapes

➡ Starting point

Show graphic **A** without showing the fraction notation below it. Ask:

- *How many equal parts has each of these rectangles been split into?* [6]
- *What fraction of the first rectangle is shaded?* [$\frac{1}{6}$] Establish that each small square is $\frac{1}{6}$ of the rectangle and that one out of six equal parts is shaded.
- *Let's find out what fraction of each of the other shapes is shaded. How many sixths are shaded in the second rectangle?* [2]
- *How do we write this as a fraction?* [$\frac{2}{6}$]

Continue in the same way for the rest of the rectangles. Reveal the line of fraction notation. Now ask:

- *What does the denominator (the bottom number) tell us?* [how many equal parts the whole is split into]
- *What does the numerator (the top number) tell us?* [how many of these equal parts are shaded]

Show graphic **B**, the rectangle that is split into eighths. Ask the pupils to identify the values of the denominator and the numerator to give the fraction $\frac{5}{8}$.

> **Key point:** The denominator (the bottom number) shows how many equal parts the whole is split into. The numerator (the top number) shows how many of the parts are being described.

🔍 Spot the mistake

Ask:

- *The statement says '$\frac{2}{3}$ is shaded'. Is this true?* [no]
- *Why isn't it true?* [The shape has five equal parts, rather than three, and two of these are shaded.] Some pupils may think that the denominator refers to the number of parts that are not shaded. Make sure that any such confusion is addressed and that all pupils understand that the denominator indicates the total number of equal parts.
- *What is the correct answer?* [$\frac{2}{5}$]
- *What fraction of the shape is not shaded?* [$\frac{3}{5}$]

✔ Good to go?

Answers: a) $\frac{3}{6}$ **b)** $\frac{4}{5}$ **c)** $\frac{2}{3}$ **d)** $\frac{3}{8}$

The pupils might give the answer $\frac{1}{2}$ for **a)**, which is also correct.

> ## Pupil book practice
> Pages 18 and 19
>
> Where questions do not involve a diagram, encourage the pupils to sketch the shape to help them visualise the fraction. The **Challenge** section involves some fractions of a turn, such as $\frac{3}{8}$ and $\frac{2}{3}$ of a full turn, including hands on a clock. If the pupils find this difficult to visualise, provide them with paper circles to divide into equal parts and compare them with the clock face or dial.

Starting point

A

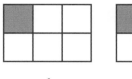   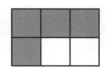 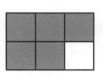 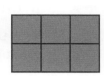

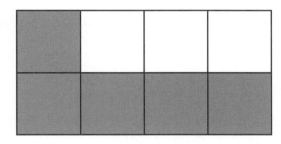

$\frac{1}{6}$ $\frac{2}{6}$ $\frac{3}{6}$ $\frac{4}{6}$ $\frac{5}{6}$ $\frac{6}{6}$

B

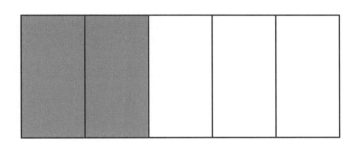

⬛ ⟵ numerator
⬛ ⟵ denominator

 Spot the mistake

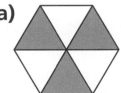

$\frac{2}{3}$ is shaded.

✔ **Good to go?**

What fraction of each shape is shaded?

a) 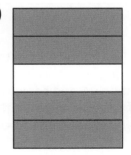   b) 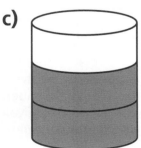   c) 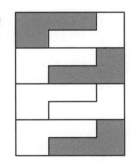   d)

Recognise tenths and count in tenths

➡ Starting point

Display graphic **A**. Ask:

- *What do we call the parts when a whole is divided into 10 equal parts?* [tenths]

Show the number line in graphic **B**, but not the fraction notation underneath. Tell the pupils that it is divided into tenths. Ask:

- *Where is the first frog?* [The pupils point to the frog.] *How can we say where on the number line it is?* [$\frac{1}{10}$] Count together in tenths from 0 until you reach the second frog.
- *Where is the second frog?* [$\frac{9}{10}$] Count together in tenths from 1 until you reach the third frog.
- *Where is the third frog?* [$1\frac{9}{10}$] Remind the pupils that a whole number and a fraction (such as $1\frac{9}{10}$) are used for non-whole numbers greater than 1. Explain that these are called 'mixed numbers'. Count together in tenths from 1 to 2 and back again. Show the fraction notation.
- *What is $\frac{10}{10}$?* [1 whole]
- *What is $\frac{20}{10}$?* [2 wholes]

Indicate a point between 1 and 2. First ask the pupils to say how many tenths it is and then ask them to describe it as a mixed number. For example, if you pointed at $\frac{15}{10}$, the pupils would give the mixed number $1\frac{5}{10}$.

It is vital that the pupils understand that the pattern of counting on in tenths goes beyond $\frac{9}{10}$ to $\frac{10}{10}$, $\frac{11}{10}$, and so on. However, there is no need to introduce the term 'improper fraction' at this stage.

> **Key point:** To count on and back in tenths. To use a whole number and a fraction (a mixed number) or a fraction with a numerator that is larger than its denominator to identify points beyond one whole.

🔍 Spot the mistake

Ask:

- *The statement says '$\frac{11}{10}$ is the same as $1\frac{2}{10}$'. Is this true?* [no]
- *Why not?* [$\frac{11}{10}$ is the same as $1\frac{1}{10}$]

✔ Good to go?

Answers: a) $\frac{8}{10}$　**b)** $1\frac{3}{10}$　**c)** 2

For extension, the pupils could be asked to give the next two numbers in each sequence.

Pupil book practice　　　　　　　　Pages 20 and 21

Here the pupils use tenths related to measures, including centimetres, metres, kilograms and litres. Many of the questions involve continuing sequences or appreciating how more than $\frac{10}{10}$ can be written as a mixed number. Question 11 and some of the **Challenge** questions explore the idea of $\frac{1}{2}$ and $\frac{5}{10}$ being equivalent. If possible, provide number lines showing tenths for the pupils who might struggle so they can use these to count forwards and backwards.

Starting point

A   1 whole

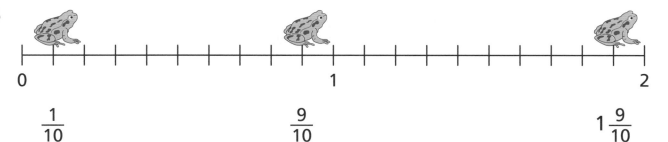

in 10 equal parts

| 1 | 2 | 3 | 4 | 5 | 6 | 7 | 8 | 9 | 10 |

B

0   1   2

$\frac{1}{10}$ $\frac{9}{10}$ $1\frac{9}{10}$

 Spot the mistake

$\frac{11}{10}$ is the same as $1\frac{2}{10}$.

✓ **Good to go?**

What number comes next?

a) $\frac{5}{10}$, $\frac{6}{10}$, $\frac{7}{10}$,

b) $\frac{9}{10}$, 1, $1\frac{1}{10}$, $1\frac{2}{10}$,

c) $2\frac{3}{10}$, $2\frac{2}{10}$, $2\frac{1}{10}$,

Recognise that tenths arise from dividing by 10

➡ Starting point

Display the three division questions without showing the circles. Ask:

- *Imagine there are 10 people and I am sharing pie between them. What is 1 pie shared equally between 10 people?* [$\frac{1}{10}$] Show the first circle and the answer $\frac{1}{10}$.

- *What if I had 2 pies to share between the 10 people? How much would they each get?* [$\frac{2}{10}$] *How could I find out?* Discuss how one way would be to cut both pies into 10 slices and give everyone a slice from both pies, so they get $\frac{2}{10}$ each. Show the second set of two circles and the answer $\frac{2}{10}$.

- *So, what do you think the answer to 3 divided by 10 is? How much would each of the 10 people get if there were 3 pies being shared?* [$\frac{3}{10}$] Remind the pupils that all 3 pies could be cut into 10 slices and each person could have a slice from each, making a total of $\frac{3}{10}$. Show the final set of circles and the fraction.

- *So, 3 ÷ 10 equals $\frac{3}{10}$. What do you notice about the numbers in the question and answer?* [The number being divided becomes the numerator of the answer and the 'divided by' number (the divisor) becomes the denominator of the answer.]

> **Key point:** Tenths are created when whole numbers are divided by 10. The number being divided becomes the numerator of the answer. The devisor becomes the denominator of the answer

🔍 Spot the mistake

Ask:

- *The statement says '7 ÷ 10 = $\frac{1}{7}$'. Is this true?* [no]
- *What mistake has been made?* [The 7 has been put on the bottom of the fraction.]
- *Which number is 7 being divided by?* [10]
- *So which number should go on the bottom?* [10]
- *What is the correct answer?* [$\frac{7}{10}$]

✔ Good to go?

Answers: a) $\frac{8}{10}$ **b)** $\frac{4}{10}$ **c)** $\frac{9}{10}$ m

> ## Pupil book practice   **Pages 22 and 23**
>
> Here the pupils can practise relating division by 10 to answers involving tenths. Problems involve measurements including metres, kilograms and litres. Note that question 23 is an extension question involving kilometres, with which some pupils may not yet be familiar. The final question also provides a challenge in that simple decimal notation of 0.2 is introduced as $\frac{2}{10}$. Tell the pupils that the digit after the decimal point shows the number of tenths. This concept will be explored more fully later in Year 3 and also in the Year 4 materials.

Starting point

$1 \div 10$ $\frac{1}{10}$

$2 \div 10$ $\frac{2}{10}$

$3 \div 10$ $\frac{3}{10}$

 Spot the mistake

$7 \div 10 = \frac{1}{7}$

 Good to go?

a) $8 \div 10 = \dfrac{}{}$

b) 4 bars of chocolate are shared between 10.

How much does each person get?

c) 9m of ribbon is cut into 10 equal parts.

How long is each part?

Use fractions as numbers on a number line

➡ Starting point

Display graphic **A**. Ask:

- *How many equal parts is each whole on this number line divided into?* [4] Draw attention to the fact that there are three marks between 0 and 1 on the line but that this represents four intervals, as shown by the shaded areas above the line. Revise counting on in quarters from 0 to 2.

Show graphic **B**. Ask:

- *How many equal parts is each whole on this number line divided into?* [5] Count on in fifths from 4 to 6. Remind the pupils again that four marks between whole numbers on the line actually represent five intervals, as shown by the shaded areas.

Show graphic **C**. Ask:

- *What about this number line? How many equal parts is each whole split into?* [10] Point to some positions on the line and ask the pupils to say each one as a mixed number, for example, $7\frac{6}{10}$.

> **Key point:** Each whole on a number line can be split into any number of equal parts. To find out how many equal parts, it is important to count the number of intervals between whole numbers, not the number of marks.

🔍 Spot the mistake

Ask:

- *The statement says that the arrow shows $2\frac{3}{4}$. Is this true?* [no]
- *What does it show?* [$2\frac{3}{5}$]
- *How do you know?* [Each whole is split into five equal parts, so this shows $2\frac{3}{5}$.]
- *Can you identify other points on the line, for example, $3\frac{2}{5}$ or $2\frac{4}{5}$?*

✔ Good to go?

Answers: A = $3\frac{1}{3}$ B = $4\frac{2}{3}$ C = $\frac{5}{8}$ D = $1\frac{3}{8}$

> ## Pupil book practice   Pages 24 and 25
>
> These questions offer opportunities for the pupils to develop an appreciation that wholes can be split into any number of equal parts. The pupils can practise identifying how many and show them as a fraction or a mixed number. Many of the questions include measurements on a ruler, including tenths of a centimetre, in preparation for decimal notation for tenths which is introduced later.
>
> If the pupils struggle with correctly identifying the numbers of intervals on a number line, encourage them to colour each interval as they count it, as shown in the **Starting point** and pupil book. Strips of paper can also be folded into equal parts and a number line drawn underneath to help these pupils see the link between fractions as areas and on number lines.

Starting point

A
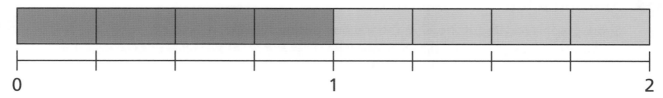

B
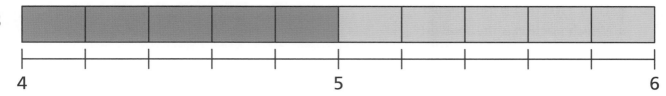

C

 Spot the mistake

   This arrow shows $2\frac{3}{4}$.

✔ **Good to go?**

What value does each letter stand for?

Compare fractions with the same denominator

➡️ **Starting point**

Show graphic **A** without showing the fraction notation below it. Ask:

- *What fraction of each rectangle is shaded?* [$\frac{1}{6}$, $\frac{2}{6}$, $\frac{3}{6}$, $\frac{4}{6}$, $\frac{5}{6}$, $\frac{6}{6}$] Establish the fraction that is shaded for each shape and reveal the notation. Point out that for $\frac{6}{6}$ the whole shape is shaded, so $\frac{6}{6}$ is equal to one whole.

- *Imagine that each rectangle is your favourite chocolate bar. The amount shaded shows how much chocolate is left. Which bar would you choose?* [the last one]

- *Which fraction is the largest?* [$\frac{6}{6}$]

- *Which fraction is the smallest?* [$\frac{1}{6}$]

Show graphic **B**. Ask:

- *Do you agree that $\frac{4}{7}$ is larger than $\frac{3}{7}$?* [yes]

Show graphic **C**. Ask:

- *What does the sign < mean?* [less than] Remind the pupils of the meaning of the less than and greater than signs (< and >).

- *What could the numerator of the first fraction be to make this statement true?* Tell the pupils that there are several possibilities. [1, 2, 3 or 4].

> **Key point:** If their denominators are the same, fractions can be compared using just their numerators. An understanding of the < and > signs is also required.

🔍 **Spot the mistake**

Ask:

- *The statement says '$\frac{5}{10} > \frac{9}{10}$'. Is this true?* [no]

- *Why isn't it true?* [As the denominators are the same, the fractions can be compared using just the numerators. It is not true that 5 is greater than 9.]

- *Can anyone make up a new statement using the greater than or less than signs that we can test?* [Example: $\frac{2}{7} < \frac{4}{7}$]

✔️ **Good to go?**

Answers: a) <   **b)** >   **c)** >

Draw attention to the fact that even fractions greater than 1, such as $\frac{6}{5}$, can be compared in this way.

> ## Pupil book practice   **Pages 26 and 27**
>
> This concept is one that the pupils can usually accept and master easily. The questions provide practice in different contexts including measurement and money problems. Question 19 in the **Challenge** section includes comparing $\frac{1}{2}$ with $\frac{5}{8}$ using the knowledge that $\frac{1}{2}$ is equivalent to $\frac{4}{8}$. Question 23 also explores the idea that, if the whole is not the same, fractions cannot be compared in this way, for example, $\frac{1}{5}$ of £100 is more than $\frac{4}{5}$ of £4.

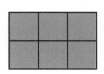

→ Starting point

A
      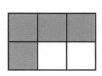 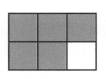

$\frac{1}{6}$ $\frac{2}{6}$ $\frac{3}{6}$ $\frac{4}{6}$ $\frac{5}{6}$ $\frac{6}{6}$

one whole

B $\frac{4}{7}$ is larger than $\frac{3}{7}$.

C $\frac{\square}{8} < \frac{5}{8}$

◯ Spot the mistake

$\frac{5}{10} > \frac{9}{10}$

✔ Good to go?

Write < or > between each pair to show which is larger.

a) $\frac{1}{3}$ ☐ $\frac{2}{3}$

b) $\frac{8}{9}$ ☐ $\frac{6}{9}$

c) $\frac{6}{5}$ ☐ $\frac{3}{5}$

Recognise fractions of a set of objects

➡️ **Starting point**

Show graphic **A**. Ask:

- *How can we decide how many smiley faces to shade if we want to shade $\frac{3}{5}$ of the faces?* [find out how many would be $\frac{1}{5}$ and then use that to work out $\frac{3}{5}$]
- *How many equal groups could we split the set into to show fifths?* Explain that the faces can be grouped into five equal groups.

Reveal graphic **B** where the faces have been grouped. Ask:

- *If each group is $\frac{1}{5}$, how many faces do we shade to show $\frac{3}{5}$?* [6]
- *How many faces would we shade to show $\frac{4}{5}$?* [8]

> **Key point:** To find fractions of sets of objects, arrange or group the items into equal groups (that is, the same number of groups as the denominator).

🔍 **Spot the mistake**

Ask:

- *The statement says '$\frac{4}{6}$ of these sweets are shaded'. Is this true?* [no]
- *Why isn't it true?* [The sweets are grouped into five equal groups not six equal groups.]
- *So what fraction of the set is shaded?* [four-fifths]
- *How do we write this as a fraction?* [$\frac{4}{5}$]

✔️ **Good to go?**

Answers: a) $\frac{2}{5}$ **b)** $\frac{3}{8}$

The pupils might give the answer $\frac{6}{15}$ for **a)** or $\frac{6}{16}$ for **b)**, which are also correct.

A further question could be asked: *What fraction of each set are not shaded?* [**a)** $\frac{3}{5}$, **b)** $\frac{5}{8}$]

Pupil book practice   Pages 28 and 29

Before the pupils tackle questions 5 and 7, it might be useful to show them how an array of squares in a grid arrangement can be grouped horizontally or vertically. For example, here 20 squares could show either fifths or quarters if grouped like this:

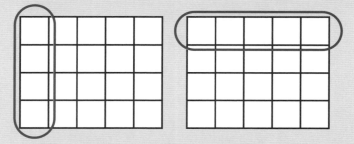

Reinforce this concept using practical resources such as folded paper or bars of chocolate. Other questions involve a range of different sets of objects being arranged or grouped into equal parts. The **Challenge** questions require the pupils to visualise this for small numbers of objects using simple fractions.

Starting point

A

Shade $\frac{3}{5}$ of this set.

B

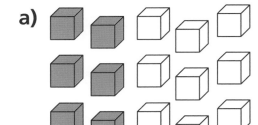

 Spot the mistake

$\frac{4}{6}$ of these sweets are shaded.

✔ **Good to go?**

What fraction of each set is shaded?

a)

b)

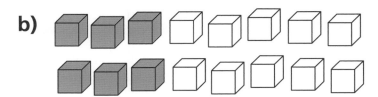

Use non-unit fractions in a variety of representations

➡️ **Starting point**

Show the **Starting point** graphic. Explain that, when describing fractions, it is important to know what the whole is. Wholes can take many forms, including lengths, shapes, sets of objects, amounts of money and numbers. Ask:

- *What is $\frac{3}{5}$ of each of these wholes?* Go through each picture in turn and discuss how the whole has been split into five equal parts to show fifths and that three of these parts are $\frac{3}{5}$. Shade or mark $\frac{3}{5}$ on each picture and discuss that $\frac{3}{5}$ of a pound is 60p.

- *Which of these fraction questions do you find easiest/hardest?* Discuss which representations the pupils find easiest or hardest to work with.

Remind the pupils that whatever the whole is, it is split into equal parts, the number of which is shown by the denominator. Provide additional examples of the representations that the pupils struggle with.

> **Key point:** Wholes can take many different forms. Whatever the whole, it can be divided into equal groups. The number of equal groups is shown by the denominator.

🔍 **Spot the mistake**

Ask:

- *The statement says 'Monday is $\frac{7}{10}$ of a week'. Is this true?* [no]
- *What is the 'whole' in the statement?* [1 week]
- *How many equal parts do we usually split one week into?* [7 days]
- *If each day is $\frac{1}{7}$ of a week, what fraction of a week is Monday?* [$\frac{1}{7}$]
- *What fraction of the week would 2 days be?* [$\frac{2}{7}$]
- *What fraction is 3 days?* [$\frac{3}{7}$]

✔️ **Good to go?**

Answers: a) $\frac{3}{4}$ **b)** $\frac{5}{8}$ **c)** $\frac{3}{5}$ **d)** $\frac{3}{10}$

The pupils might give the answer $\frac{12}{20}$ for **c)**, which is also correct.

> ## Pupil book practice   **Pages 32 and 33**
>
> This time there is mixed practice of a full range of representations of fractions including number lines, sets of objects, areas of shapes, numbers, measurements and amounts of money. The **Challenge** questions encourage the pupils to begin to consider how many times greater a non-unit fraction (such as $\frac{3}{5}$) is than its related unit fraction (such as $\frac{1}{5}$). This leads to recognising how many times greater a non-unit fraction of an amount will be than the unit fraction of the same amount, for example, if you know that $\frac{1}{3}$ of an amount is 10p, how much is $\frac{2}{3}$ of the same amount?

Starting point

$\frac{3}{5}$ of …

a whole shape   a whole set of items   a whole pizza

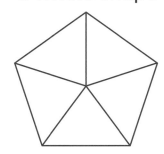      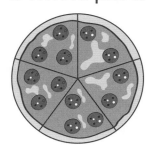

a whole line
or number

a whole bar
of chocolate   a whole pound

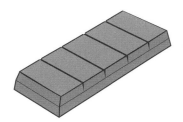   

 Spot the mistake

Monday is $\frac{7}{10}$ of a week.

 Good to go?

What fraction does each show?

a)    b)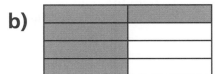

c) 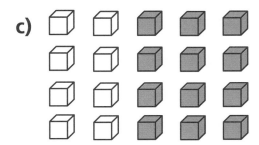   d) I scored 3 out of 10 in the test.

Recognise fractions showing the same amount

➡️ **Starting point**

Show graphic **A**. Ask:

● *What fraction of the first rectangle is shaded?* [$\frac{1}{4}$]
● *What fraction of the second rectangle is shaded?* [$\frac{2}{8}$]
● *Which is greater?* $\frac{1}{4}$ *of a shape or* $\frac{2}{8}$ *of it?* Encourage the pupils to see that both fractions are the same amount.

Repeat, but ask what fraction of each rectangle is unshaded. [$\frac{3}{4}$ and $\frac{6}{8}$] Again, establish that the two fractions sound different and are written differently, but that they actually stand for the same amount.

Show graphic **B**. Ask:

● *What are the arrows on the number line pointing to?* [$\frac{4}{5}$ and $\frac{8}{10}$] Again, explain that different fractions can stand for the same amount.

The word 'equivalent' is introduced in the next unit, but it is not needed until then. This allows the pupils to explore the idea without getting stuck on a difficult new word.

> **Key point:** Fractions that are written using different numbers can stand for the same amount, such as $\frac{3}{6}$ and $\frac{1}{2}$.

🔍 **Spot the mistake**

Ask:

● *The statement says that* $\frac{2}{5}$ *is equal to* $\frac{1}{10}$. *Is this true?* [no]
● *What is the correct answer?* [$\frac{2}{5} = \frac{4}{10}$] Draw a number line to show that $\frac{2}{5}$ is equivalent to $\frac{4}{10}$.
● *Can you tell me some other pairs of fractions that stand for the same amount?* [Example: $\frac{1}{3} = \frac{2}{6}$]

✔️ **Good to go?**

Answers: a) $\frac{4}{8}$ **b)** $\frac{3}{6}$ **c)** $\frac{2}{4}$

All three representations show the same amount as $\frac{1}{2}$.

> ## Pupil book practice   **Pages 34 and 35**
>
> Where questions do not involve a diagram, encourage the pupils to sketch the shape or draw a number line to help them visualise the fraction. Question 16 introduces the idea that more than two fractions can show the same amount. The next unit will introduce the vocabulary of equivalence and equivalent fractions and provides more opportunity for the pupils to develop these ideas in a range of contexts and representations.

Starting point

shaded   unshaded

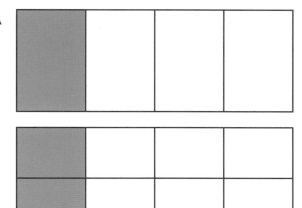

A

B

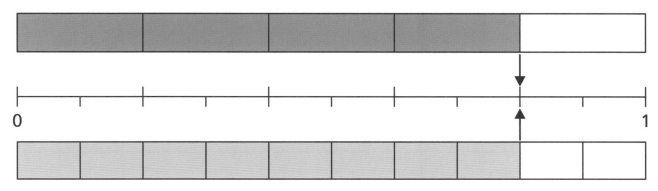

 ## Spot the mistake

$$\frac{2}{5} = \frac{1}{10}$$

 ## Good to go?

Write the fractions shown.

a) 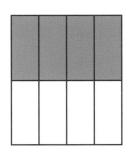   b) 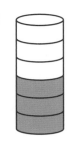   c)

Which show the same amount as $\frac{1}{2}$?

Find equivalent fractions using a fraction wall

➡ **Starting point**

Show the fraction wall in the **Starting point** graphic. Explain that each strip is worth one whole. Count in halves, then thirds, quarters, sixths and eighths as you point to each section of the fraction wall. Ask:

● *How many quarters are shaded?* [1]
● *How do we write this fraction?* [$\frac{1}{4}$]
● *How many eighths are shaded?* [2]
● *How do we write this fraction?* [$\frac{2}{8}$]
● *Are they the same amount?* [yes]

Introduce the term 'equivalent', meaning 'of the same value' or 'the same amount'.

Show the first statement. Invite the pupils to read the statement aloud to become familiar with the term 'equivalent'.

Demonstrate how to find $\frac{2}{3}$ on the fraction wall and shade the first two thirds. Ask:

● *What other equal parts could we shade to show the same amount?* [$\frac{4}{6}$] Shade $\frac{4}{6}$ and show that the fractions $\frac{4}{6}$ and $\frac{2}{3}$ are equivalent.

Reveal the second statement and reiterate the meaning of the term 'equivalent'.

> **Key point:** Fractions that are written using different numbers and stand for the same amount are called 'equivalent fractions'. Fraction walls can be used to find equivalent fractions.

🔍 **Spot the mistake**

Ask:

● *The statement says '$\frac{3}{4}$ is equivalent to $\frac{7}{8}$'. Is this true?* [no] Use the fraction wall to establish that $\frac{7}{8}$ is greater than $\frac{3}{4}$.
● *What fraction is $\frac{3}{4}$ equivalent to?* [$\frac{6}{8}$] Use the fraction wall to demonstrate that $\frac{6}{8}$ is equivalent to $\frac{3}{4}$.
● *Can you give me some other fractions from the fraction wall that stand for the same amount?* [Example: $\frac{1}{2} = \frac{3}{6}$]

✔ **Good to go?**

Answers: a) $\frac{2}{6}$ **b)** $\frac{2}{4}$ **c)** $\frac{3}{6}$ **d)** $\frac{2}{3}$

The pupils can use the fraction wall in the **Starting point** to help them with this exercise.

> ## Pupil book practice   **Pages 36 and 37**
>
> The **Get started** section involves questions that can be answered using the fraction wall given in the **Key point**. The later sections involve other fractions, including fifths and tenths. Provide the pupils with a fraction wall (available to download from the Schofield & Sims website) or encourage them to visualise fractions of shapes when trying to find equivalents. The pupils need to be confident in finding fractions as sets of objects or quantities for the **Challenge** section.

Starting point

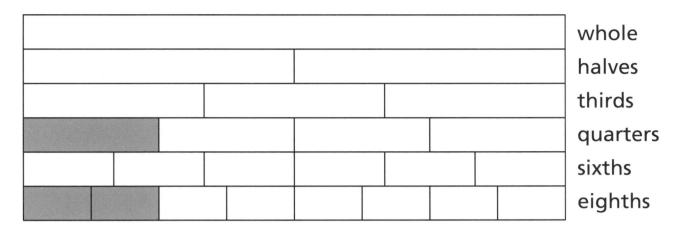

$\frac{1}{4}$ is equivalent to $\frac{2}{8}$.

$\frac{2}{3}$ is equivalent to $\frac{4}{6}$.

 Spot the mistake

$\frac{3}{4}$ is equivalent to $\frac{7}{8}$.

 Good to go?

Work out the missing numbers.

a) $\frac{1}{3}$ is equivalent to $\frac{\square}{6}$.

b) $\frac{4}{8}$ is equivalent to $\frac{\square}{4}$.

c) $\frac{1}{2}$ is equivalent to $\frac{\square}{6}$.

d) $\frac{4}{6}$ is equivalent to $\frac{\square}{3}$.

Add fractions with the same denominator

➡ Starting point

Show graphic **A**. Ask:

- *What fraction of the first shape is shaded?* [$\frac{1}{8}$]
- *What does the denominator (the bottom number) show us?* [It shows that the whole is split into eight equal parts.]
- *How many eighths of the second shape are shaded?* [$\frac{4}{8}$]
- *If we add $\frac{1}{8}$ and $\frac{4}{8}$, what is the total?* [$\frac{5}{8}$]
- *What do you notice about the denominator of the answer?* [It is the same as the denominators in the question.]
- *What do you notice about the numerator of the answer?* [It is the total of the numerators in the question.]

Show graphic **B**. Ask:

- *Which point on the number line shows $\frac{1}{5}$?* [The pupils point to $\frac{1}{5}$.] Show how the line is split into fifths (five equal parts) by counting the intervals and point to $\frac{1}{5}$.
- *If we count on $\frac{3}{5}$ from $\frac{1}{5}$ where do we end up?* [$\frac{4}{5}$]
- *What do you notice about the denominator of the answer?* [It is the same as the denominators in the question.]
- *What do you notice about the numerator of the answer?* [It is the total of the numerators in the question.]

> **Key point:** When adding fractions that have the same denominator, only the numerators are added. The denominator of the answer is always the same.

🔍 Spot the mistake

Ask:

- *The statement says '$\frac{2}{5} + \frac{2}{5} = \frac{4}{10}$'. Is this true?* [no]
- *What is the mistake?* [The denominators have been added. This is incorrect, because only the numerators should be added.]
- *What should the answer be?* [$\frac{4}{5}$]

✔ Good to go?

Answers: a) $\frac{2}{3}$ **b)** $\frac{3}{4}$ **c)** $\frac{5}{6}$

> ## Pupil book practice   **Pages 38 and 39**
>
> The **Challenge** questions include some equivalence work where the pupils should notice that $\frac{5}{10}$ is equal to $\frac{1}{2}$ and so on. Some problems involve finding fractions of measures, for example, finding $\frac{3}{4}$ of 1 kilogram in grams. Question 21 includes the decimal 0.4 – explain to the pupils that this is another way of writing $\frac{4}{10}$.

Starting point

A

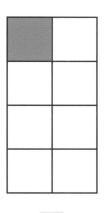   +   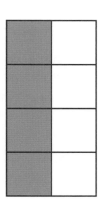   =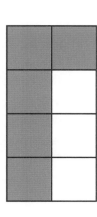

$$\frac{}{8} \quad + \quad \frac{}{8} \quad = \quad \frac{}{}$$

B

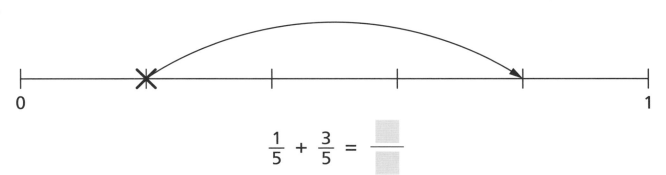

$$\frac{1}{5} + \frac{3}{5} = \frac{}{}$$

 Spot the mistake

$$\frac{2}{5} + \frac{2}{5} = \frac{4}{10}$$

 Good to go?

a) $\frac{1}{3} + \frac{1}{3} = \frac{}{}$

b) $\frac{1}{4} + \frac{2}{4} = \frac{}{}$

c) $\frac{1}{6} + \frac{4}{6} = \frac{}{}$

Subtract fractions with the same denominator

➡ **Starting point**

Show the calculation in graphic **A**. Ask:

- *What is $\frac{7}{8}$ take away $\frac{2}{8}$?* Reveal the diagram to show that $\frac{7}{8}$ were shaded and then $\frac{2}{8}$ were crossed out. Use this to help the pupils reach the answer $\frac{5}{8}$.
- *What do you notice about the denominator of the answer?* [It is the same as the denominators in the question.]
- *What do you notice about the numerator of the answer?* [It is the difference between the numerators in the question.]

Show graphic **B**. Ask:

- *Where is $\frac{4}{5}$ on the number line?* [The pupils point to $\frac{4}{5}$.]
- *If we count back $\frac{2}{5}$, where do we end up?* [$\frac{2}{5}$]
- *What do you notice about the denominator of the answer?* [It is the same as the denominators in the question.]
- *What do you notice about the numerator of the answer?* [It is the difference between the numerators in the question.]

> **Key point:** When subtracting fractions that have the same denominator, only the numerators are subtracted. The denominator of the answer is always the same.

🔍 **Spot the mistake**

Ask:

- *The statement says '$\frac{7}{10} - \frac{2}{10} = \frac{5}{0}$'. Is this true?* [no]
- *What is the mistake?* [The denominators have been subtracted. This is not correct, because only the numerators should be subtracted.]
- *What should the answer be?* [$\frac{5}{10}$] Remind the pupils that $\frac{5}{10}$ is equivalent to $\frac{1}{2}$, so the answer $\frac{1}{2}$ could also be given.

✔ **Good to go?**

Answers: a) $\frac{1}{3}$ **b)** $\frac{7}{10}$ **c)** $\frac{3}{6}$

The pupils might give the answer $\frac{1}{2}$ for **c)**, which is also correct.

> ## Pupil book practice   **Pages 40 and 41**
>
> Ensure the pupils know the words 'difference' and 'decrease' before tackling the questions. The **Challenge** questions include some equivalence work where the pupils should be able to say that $\frac{6}{9}$ is equivalent to $\frac{2}{3}$, for example. The decimal 0.4 is used in question 22 so the pupils may need to be reminded that 0.4 means 4 tenths or $\frac{4}{10}$.

Starting point

A $\frac{7}{8} - \frac{2}{8} = \dfrac{}{}$

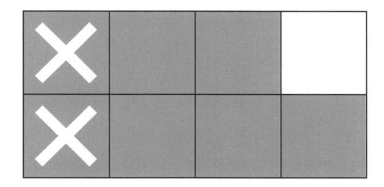

B

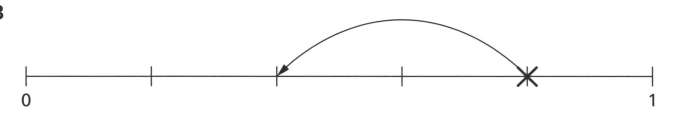

$$\frac{4}{5} - \frac{2}{5} = \dfrac{}{}$$

 Spot the mistake

$$\frac{7}{10} - \frac{2}{10} = \frac{5}{0}$$

 Good to go?

a) $\frac{2}{3} - \frac{1}{3} = \dfrac{}{}$

b) $\frac{9}{10} - \frac{2}{10} = \dfrac{}{}$

c) $\frac{5}{6} - \frac{2}{6} = \dfrac{}{}$

Solve problems with measures

➡ Starting point

Remind the pupils that wholes can take many forms including lengths, shapes, sets of objects, amounts of money or numbers. Explain that the focus of the lesson is wholes as units of measurement such as metres, kilograms, litres and centimetres.

Show graphic **A**. Ask:

● *Can anyone point to $\frac{1}{2}$/$\frac{3}{4}$/$\frac{2}{10}$ of a metre on these metre sticks?* Go through each measurement in turn and discuss how the whole has been split into the number of equal parts as shown by the denominator.

Show graphic **B**. Ask similar questions for $\frac{3}{4}$ of a litre and the mixed number $1\frac{3}{4}$. Ensure the pupils understand that the 1 represents a whole.

Show graphic **C**. Ask:

● *If these 5 weights make 1 kilogram, how many of these weights would be $\frac{2}{5}$ of a kilogram?* [2]

Show graphic **D**. Explain that the arrow is pointing to 0.9cm. The pupils may have previously encountered decimal notation for tenths. In preparation for work in Year 4, ask:

● *Can anyone explain what 0.9 means and why?* [When a number has a decimal point, the digit that follows it shows how many tenths there are.] Explain that decimals are just a different way of writing fractions and that it is also correct to say that the arrow is pointing to $\frac{9}{10}$ cm.

> **Key point:** Wholes can take many different forms, including units of measurement. Whatever the whole, it can be divided into equal groups. The number of equal groups is shown by the denominator.

🔍 Spot the mistake

Ask:

● *How do you say each of these measurements?* [two-fifths of a kilogram, two and one-fifth of a kilogram, one and four-fifths of a kilogram]
● *Is the circled measurement the heaviest mass?* [no]
● *Which is the heaviest mass* [$2\frac{1}{5}$kg]
● *How do you know?* [The mass has two whole kilograms and a fraction of a whole kilogram. The other measurements have only one or no wholes.]

✔ Good to go?

Answers: a) 50cm   b) $\frac{7}{10}$m   c) $2\frac{1}{4}$l

Pupil book practice   **Pages 42 and 43**

There are a variety of fraction and mixed number problems where wholes are units of measurement. The range of question types from all the units serves as revision of many of the ideas encountered. The pupils will need to know the number of centimetres in a metre and the number of minutes in an hour. Some decimal notation with tenths is included in the **Now try these** section.

Starting point

A metres

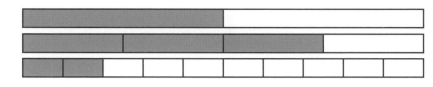

B litres

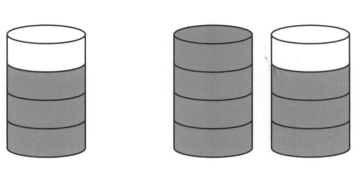

C a kilogram

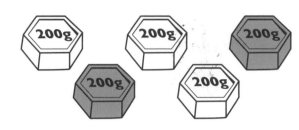

D centimetres

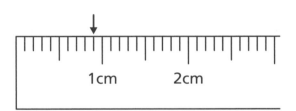

 Spot the mistake

The heaviest mass is circled. $\frac{2}{5}$kg $2\frac{1}{5}$kg $\boxed{1\frac{4}{5}kg}$

✔ **Good to go?**

a) How many centimetres is half a metre?

b) 0.3m means $\frac{3}{10}$m. What fraction of a metre is 0.7m?

c) What is $\frac{1}{4}$l more than 2l?

Recognise quarters as fractions of shapes

Key point

$\frac{1}{4}$ is the same as **one-quarter**.

numerator   ⟶ 1
denominator ⟶ $\frac{}{4}$

The **4** on the bottom of the fraction (the **denominator**) shows **how many equal parts a whole is split into**.

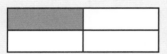

$\frac{1}{4}$ of this shape is purple. **1 out of 4 equal parts** is purple.

Get started

1 True or false? $\frac{1}{4}$ of the shape is purple.

a)   True ✓   False ☐

b)    True ☐   False ✓

2 What fraction of this shape is purple?

$\frac{1}{4}$

3 Write the denominator of one-quarter. ___4___

4 Write the numerator of one-quarter. ___1___

5 True or false? One-quarter is purple.

True ☐   False ✓

6 Tick the shape with $\frac{1}{4}$ shaded.

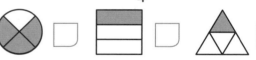 ✓

7 How many equal parts is a shape divided into to show quarters?

___4___

8 Write $\frac{1}{4}$ in words.

___one-quarter___

Now try these

9 Tick the two shapes which have $\frac{1}{4}$ shaded. ☐ ☐ ✓ ✓

10 True or false? $\frac{1}{4}$ is half of $\frac{1}{2}$.   True ✓   False ☐

11 How many quarters make a half? ___2___ quarters

12 How many people can each have $\frac{1}{4}$ of Jo's birthday cake? ___4___

13 What number will the arrow point to after a $\frac{1}{4}$ turn clockwise? ____1____

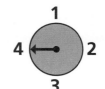

14 Write one-quarter as a fraction. ___$\frac{1}{4}$___

15 True or false? $\frac{1}{4} + \frac{1}{4} = \frac{1}{2}$ True ✓   False ☐

16 What fraction of this shape is purple? ___$\frac{3}{4}$___

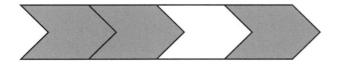

Challenge

17 What number does the minute hand of a clock point to at 'quarter past'? ____3____

18 What number does the minute hand of a clock point to at 'quarter to'? ____9____

19 A pizza is cut into four equal slices. What fraction of the whole pizza is one slice? ___$\frac{1}{4}$___

20 $\frac{1}{4}$ litre is poured into this empty 1 litre container. Which letter will the liquid reach? ____D____

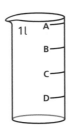

21 A chocolate bar has 8 chunks. Sam eats one-quarter of the bar. How many chunks does he eat? ____2____

22 A 1m plank of wood is cut into four equal lengths. What fraction of a metre are three of these lengths together? ___$\frac{3}{4}$___ m

23 Joshua spent $\frac{1}{2}$ hour eating the main course of his meal and $\frac{1}{4}$ hour eating dessert.

a) What fraction of an hour did he spend eating altogether? ___$\frac{3}{4}$___ hr

b) How many minutes is this? ____45____ min

24 The dial on a washing machine has 8 settings. The arrow is pointing to 4. What number will it point to after a quarter turn clockwise? ____6____

Recognise halves and quarters of sets

Key point

Fractions can be used to show the parts of **sets of objects**.
These cards are sorted into 4 equal-sized groups.

This shows that $\frac{1}{4}$ of the cards are purple and $\frac{3}{4}$ of the cards are white.

There are 8 cards so $\frac{1}{4}$ of 8 cards = 2 cards and $\frac{3}{4}$ of 8 cards = 6 cards.

Get started

1 Colour $\frac{1}{4}$ of this set of cubes.

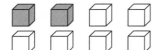

2 What fraction of the ants are on the leaf? $\frac{1}{2}$

3 Tick more squares so that half the squares in this grid are ticked.

✓	✓	✓	✓	
			✓	

4 What fraction of the horses are wearing saddles?

$\frac{1}{4}$

5 A bus has 12 children on it. Six are girls. What fraction are girls?

$\frac{1}{2}$

6 Find one-quarter of 16.

$\underline{\quad 4 \quad}$ IIII   IIII   IIII   IIII

7 Write the missing number.

$\boxed{\frac{1}{2}}$ of 20 sweets is 10 sweets.

8 What fraction of these marbles are purple?

$\frac{1}{2}$

Now try these

9 What fraction of the grid is: **a)** purple? $\frac{1}{4}$ or $\frac{3}{12}$

                 b) white? $\frac{3}{4}$ or $\frac{9}{12}$

10 There are six steps. Aisha is on the third step. What fraction of the way up the steps is she? $\frac{1}{2}$

11 True or false? Harry ate 2 of the 8 cupcakes in a box. He has eaten one-quarter of them.   True $\boxed{✓}$ False $\boxed{}$

12 Tick the tile pattern which shows $\frac{1}{4}$ purple.

 ☐   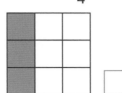 ☐   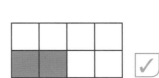 ☑   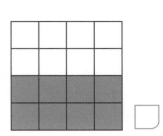 ☐

13 Leah pours 8 cups of juice. 2 cups have orange juice. The rest have apple juice. What fraction of the cups have apple juice? $\frac{3}{4}$ or $\frac{6}{8}$

14 Ethan has 8 pound coins. He spends half of them. How much money has he now? £ ___4___

15 A bag contains 6 red apples, 3 yellow apples and 3 green apples.

What fraction of the apples are: **a)** red? $\frac{1}{2}$ or $\frac{6}{12}$ **b)** green? $\frac{1}{4}$ or $\frac{3}{12}$

16 A small wall is made from 14 bricks in a row. How many bricks in half a row? ___7___

Challenge

17 A book has 20 pages. Ali has read 5 pages. What fraction of the book has Ali read? $\frac{1}{4}$ or $\frac{5}{20}$

18 Yusuf works for 21 of the 28 days in February.
What fraction of the days in February does Yusuf not work? $\frac{1}{4}$ or $\frac{7}{28}$

19 Three-quarters of the beads
on a necklace are silver.
How many beads are silver? ___12___

20 There are 18 sweets in half a packet of sweets.
How many sweets are there in a quarter of a packet? ___9___

21 How many minutes in:

    a) half an hour? ___30___ min

    b) one-quarter of an hour? ___15___ min

    c) three-quarters of an hour? ___45___ min

22 Alice has one pound in 1p coins. She sorts the coins into four equal piles.

What is the value of the coins in one pile? ___25___ p

23 A tennis club has 40 children. $\frac{1}{4}$ of them are boys. How many are girls? ___30___

24 Four teams play in a tournament. Two of the teams wear red.
Write two different fractions to show what fraction of the teams wear red. ___$\frac{1}{2}$___ or ___$\frac{2}{4}$___

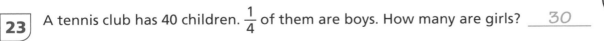

Count up and down in halves and quarters

Key point

When counting in halves from 0, every other number is a whole number:

$0, \frac{1}{2}, 1, 1\frac{1}{2}, 2, 2\frac{1}{2}, 3 \ldots$

When counting in quarters from 0 remember $\frac{2}{4}$ and $\frac{1}{2}$ have the same value:

$0, \frac{1}{4}, \frac{2}{4}, \frac{3}{4}, 1, 1\frac{1}{4}, 1\frac{2}{4}, 1\frac{3}{4}, 2, 2\frac{1}{4}, 2\frac{2}{4}, 2\frac{3}{4}, 3 \ldots$

Both are correct.

$0, \frac{1}{4}, \frac{1}{2}, \frac{3}{4}, 1, 1\frac{1}{4}, 1\frac{1}{2}, 1\frac{3}{4}, 2, 2\frac{1}{4}, 2\frac{1}{2}, 2\frac{3}{4}, 3 \ldots$

Get started

1 How many faces are purple?

$2\frac{1}{2}$

2 What number is the arrow pointing to?

$\frac{3}{4}$

3 What is one-quarter more than $2\frac{1}{2}$?

$2\frac{3}{4}$

4 What is one-quarter less than four wholes?

$3\frac{3}{4}$

5 Write the missing number in this sequence.

$0, \frac{1}{2}, 1, 1\frac{1}{2}, \underline{\quad 2 \quad}, 2\frac{1}{2}$

6 What is $\frac{1}{4}$ more than $1\frac{1}{4}$?

$1\frac{2}{4}$ or $1\frac{1}{2}$

7 Write the next number in the sequence.

$3, 3\frac{1}{4}, 3\frac{1}{2}, 3\frac{3}{4}, 4, \underline{\quad 4\frac{1}{4} \quad}$

8 What are eight halves? $\underline{\quad 4 \quad}$ wholes

Now try these

9 When counting on in halves, what number comes after 3? $\underline{\quad 3\frac{1}{2} \quad}$

10 What is $1\frac{3}{4} + \frac{1}{4}$? $\underline{\quad 2 \quad}$

11 Write the next two numbers in this sequence. $7\frac{1}{2}, 7\frac{1}{4}, 7, 6\frac{3}{4}, 6\frac{1}{2}, \underline{\quad 6\frac{1}{4} \quad}, \underline{\quad 6 \quad}$

12 How many quarters are in $2\frac{1}{2}$? $\underline{\quad 10 \quad}$ quarters

13 How many halves in six wholes? ____12____ halves

14 How heavy is the pumpkin?

____$3\frac{1}{2}$____ kg

15 Look at the number line. Write the values of A and B.   A = ____$7\frac{1}{4}$____   B = ____$8\frac{3}{4}$____

```
 |——+——+——+——+——+——+——+——+——|
 7   ↑          8          ↑   9
     A                     B
```

16 Count back ten-quarters from 5. What number do you reach? ____$2\frac{1}{2}$____

Challenge

17 Lucy counts on an even number of halves from 0. Circle the number she finishes on.

$5\frac{1}{2}$ $6\frac{1}{4}$ ③ $3\frac{3}{4}$ $4\frac{1}{2}$

18 Each of Eva's steps is half a metre apart when she walks.
If she takes 9 steps, how far has she walked? ____$4\frac{1}{2}$____ m

$\frac{1}{2}$ m

19 What number is two-quarters more than $4\frac{3}{4}$? ____$5\frac{1}{4}$____

20 What is $7\frac{1}{2} - \frac{3}{4}$? ____$6\frac{3}{4}$____

21 A fountain pours $\frac{1}{4}$ litre of water every second.
How much water will it pour in 11 seconds? ____$2\frac{3}{4}$____ l

22 Jack is at the cinema. The adverts last $\frac{1}{2}$ hour and the film lasts $1\frac{3}{4}$ hours.
How long does he watch these in total?

____$2\frac{1}{4}$____ hr

23 Amir weighs $20\frac{1}{2}$ kg. Chloe weighs $3\frac{3}{4}$ kg less. How much does Chloe weigh? ____$16\frac{3}{4}$____ kg

24 How many quarters greater than $8\frac{1}{2}$ is 10? ____6____ quarters

Understand fractions with the numerator 1

Key point

$\frac{1}{3}$ is **one-third**.   The **3** on the bottom of the fraction (the **denominator**) shows **how many equal parts a whole is split into.**

To find the **denominator**, see how many equal parts the whole is split into. If a whole is split into **3** equal parts, each part is $\frac{1}{3}$ (**one-third**). If it is split into **5** equal parts each part is $\frac{1}{5}$ (**one-fifth**) and so on.

Get started

1 How many equal parts has this shape been divided into?

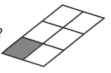

_____6_____

2 Tick the square that is $\frac{1}{3}$ purple.

3 Colour one-fifth of this star.

4 A cake is cut into 8 equal slices. What fraction of the cake is 1 slice? ____$\frac{1}{8}$____

5 What fraction of this pizza is each slice?

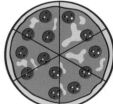

____$\frac{1}{6}$____

6 Ben scored 1 out of 5 points in a quiz. Write this as a fraction.

____$\frac{1}{5}$____

7 How many ninths make up one whole?

_____9_____ ninths

8 A chocolate bar has five equal-sized chunks. Write in words what fraction of the bar is one chunk.

_____one-fifth_____

Now try these

9 Tick the circle that has about $\frac{1}{3}$ shaded.

10 A melon is cut into seven equal slices. What fraction of the melon is one slice? ____$\frac{1}{7}$____

11 How many eighths make: **a)** a whole? ____8____ eighths **b)** a half? ____4____ eighths

12 How many people can each have a sixth of Sara's birthday cake? ____6____

13 What fraction of these beads are white? $\frac{1}{7}$

14 True or false? One-fifth of this shape is purple.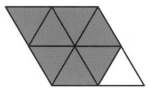

True ☐   False ✓

15 What fraction of this shape is not purple?

$\frac{1}{8}$

16 What fraction of this cuboid is each cube? Write the fraction in words.

one-sixth

Challenge

17 A tabletop is covered in tiles. Eight tiles are white and one is green. What fraction of the tiles are green? $\frac{1}{9}$

18 A 1m stick is cut into five equal lengths. What fraction of a metre is each length? $\frac{1}{5}$ m

19 One-quarter of an hour is 15 minutes. How many minutes is one-third of an hour?

20 min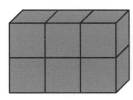

20 The dial on a dishwasher has 8 settings. The arrow points to 6. What will it point to after an eighth of a turn clockwise? 7

21 Isaac pours one cup of apple juice and four cups of orange juice into a jug. What fraction of the mixture is apple juice? $\frac{1}{5}$

22 The minute hand of a clock moves from 12 to 1. What fraction of the clock face has the hand moved? $\frac{1}{12}$

23 If one whole is divided by 3, what fraction do you get?

$1 \div 3 = \dfrac{1}{3}$

24 Amy makes a hanging decoration using only paper pentagons of the same size. She uses 5 red, 2 gold and 1 silver pentagon. What fraction of the decoration is:

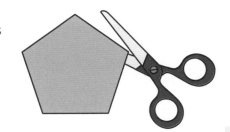

a) silver? $\frac{1}{8}$ b) not silver? $\frac{7}{8}$

Compare fractions with the numerator 1

Key point

The **denominator** shows **how many equal parts a whole is split into**.

The **more parts** the whole is split into, the **smaller** each part is.

For fractions with the **numerator 1**, the **larger** the **denominator** the **smaller** the **value of the fraction**.

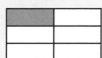 $\frac{1}{6}$ is smaller than $\frac{1}{4}$.

$$\frac{1}{6} < \frac{1}{4}$$

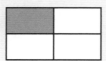

Get started

1 True or false? $\frac{1}{4}$ is larger than $\frac{1}{2}$.

True ☐   False ✓

2 Write in words the name of the larger fraction shown.

_____one-third_____

3 Write in digits the smaller fraction shown.

$\frac{1}{4}$

4 True or false? $\frac{1}{3}$ is greater than $\frac{1}{2}$.

True ☐   False ✓

5 Which makes larger slices?

A pie cut into 4 slices. ✓

The same pie cut into 5 slices. ☐

6 Circle the fraction that is smaller than one-quarter. $\frac{1}{3}$ $\frac{1}{2}$ $\boxed{\frac{1}{5}}$

7 True or false? $\frac{1}{3} < \frac{1}{2}$

True ✓   False ☐

8 Use either the < or > sign to show which is larger.

$\frac{1}{6}$ $\boxed{<}$ $\frac{1}{4}$

Now try these

9 Is one-eighth of a kilogram more or less than one-quarter of a kilogram? _____less_____

10 Tick to show how the fractions in this sequence are ordered: $\frac{1}{2}, \frac{1}{3}, \frac{1}{4}, \frac{1}{5}, \frac{1}{6}$

smallest to largest ☐   largest to smallest ✓

11 Which letter on the number line shows:

0   A   B   C   1

a) $\frac{1}{2}$? _____C_____   b) $\frac{1}{8}$? _____A_____

c) Which of the two fractions is larger? _____$\frac{1}{2}$_____

12 Two jugs are the same size. Jug A is $\frac{1}{8}$ full. Jug B is $\frac{1}{6}$ full. Which jug contains more? ___B___

13 Tick the longer time. $\frac{1}{6}$ of an hour ☐ $\frac{1}{2}$ an hour ✓

14 Write these fractions from smallest to largest:

$\frac{1}{7}$ $\frac{1}{3}$ $\frac{1}{9}$ _$\frac{1}{9}$_   _$\frac{1}{7}$_   _$\frac{1}{3}$_

15 Callum has a box of chocolates. He gives $\frac{1}{4}$ to Sam and $\frac{1}{6}$ to Li.

Who gets more chocolates – Sam or Li? _____Sam_____

16 Write these fractions from smallest to largest:

$\frac{1}{4}$ $\frac{1}{2}$ $\frac{1}{8}$ $\frac{1}{6}$ _$\frac{1}{8}$_   _$\frac{1}{6}$_   _$\frac{1}{4}$_   _$\frac{1}{2}$_

Challenge

17 Alfie cuts two pizzas of the same size into slices. He cuts one into fifths and the other into sixths. Alfie eats one of the smaller slices. What fraction of a whole pizza does he eat? _$\frac{1}{6}$_

18 What is the missing number if this fraction is larger than one-fifth but smaller than one-third? $\frac{1}{4}$

19 Emma walked for one-quarter of a kilometre. Rosie walked for one-sixth of a kilometre. Who walked further? _____Emma_____

20 Draw ticks on one-eighth of this grid and crosses on one-sixth. Are there more squares with ticks or crosses? _____crosses_____

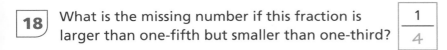

21 Cross out one of these fractions so that the rest are in order of size: $\frac{1}{6}$ $\frac{1}{4}$ $\frac{1}{3}$ $\cancel{\frac{1}{5}}$ $\frac{1}{2}$

22 On this jug, which letter shows:

a) $\frac{1}{4}$ of a litre? ___Z___

b) $\frac{1}{5}$ of a litre? ___E___

23 A bag contains 24 nuts. Aaron eats $\frac{1}{3}$ of them. Billy eats $\frac{1}{8}$ of them. Safa eats $\frac{1}{2}$ of them.

a) Who eats the most nuts? _____Safa_____

b) How many more nuts does Aaron eat than Billy? ___5___

24 Finn mixed some paint. He used $\frac{1}{3}$l of white paint, $\frac{1}{5}$l of red paint and $\frac{1}{4}$l of blue paint. Tick the statement that is true. He used:

more red than blue. ☐   more blue than white. ☐   more white than blue. ✓

Recognise unit fractions as a division of a quantity

Key point

If the top number (the **numerator**) of a fraction is **1**, it is called a **unit fraction**.

$\frac{1}{3}, \frac{1}{12}, \frac{1}{5}, \frac{1}{9}, \frac{1}{7}$ These are called **unit fractions**.

To find a **unit fraction** of a quantity, divide the **quantity** by the **denominator**.

numerator ⟶ $\frac{1}{10}$ of £50 = £50 ÷ 10 = £5 $\frac{1}{9}$ of 27m = 27m ÷ 9 = 3m
denominator ⟶

Get started

1 Find $\frac{1}{5}$ of 25cm.

_____5_____ cm

2 Find $\frac{1}{10}$ of 70kg.

_____7_____ kg

3 What length is one-fifth of this line?

_____2_____ cm

0   10cm

4 Find $\frac{1}{2}$ of 74ml.

_____37_____ ml

5 Find one-quarter of 12p.

_____3_____ p

6 Find $\frac{1}{10}$ of 40g.

_____4_____ g

7 Write the missing number.

$\frac{1}{\boxed{2}}$ of 12m = 6m

8 Add $\frac{1}{8}$ of 24p to $\frac{1}{4}$ of 24p.

_____9_____ p

Now try these

9 A metre of ribbon costs £4.
What length of ribbon would you get for £1? _____$\frac{1}{4}$_____ m

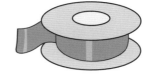

10 How much less than 8cm is $\frac{1}{10}$ of 60cm? _____2_____ cm

11 Find $\frac{1}{3}$ of £9 plus $\frac{1}{3}$ of £6. £_____5_____

12 A right angle is 90°.
How many degrees is half a right angle? _____45_____ °

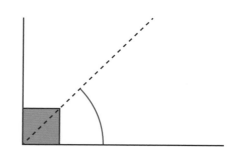

13 What is one-third of 27? _____9_____

14 James earns £600. He gives one-tenth of his wages to charity.
How much does he give to charity? £_____60_____

15 Dhruv takes a quarter of the money out of each of these boxes.
How much does he take in total? £_____5_____

16 What is one-fifth of £60? £_____12_____

Challenge

17 One-quarter of a class of 28 children wear glasses.
How many wear glasses? _____7_____

18 The length of a rectangle is 15cm. Its width is one-third of its length.
Find the perimeter of the rectangle. _____40_____ cm

15cm

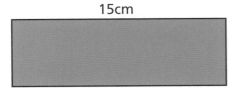

19 Find the difference in kilograms between $\frac{1}{4}$ of 32kg and $\frac{1}{8}$ of 48kg. _____2_____ kg

20 | $\frac{1}{3}$ of £36 | $\frac{1}{8}$ of £40 | $\frac{1}{10}$ of £110 |

Look at the fractions above. What is the value of the:

a) largest of these amounts? £_____12_____   **b)** smallest of these amounts? £_____5_____

21 How many minutes is $\frac{1}{6}$ of an hour? _____10_____ min

22 Write the missing number to match this picture.

18l

$\dfrac{1}{3}$ of 18l = 6l

6l   6l   6l

23 Amber divides 60 by 5 to help her answer the question 'What fraction of an hour is 5 minutes?'
Write her answer. _____$\frac{1}{12}$_____ hr

24 A 3m length of string is cut into 10 equal pieces. Write the length of each piece:

a) as a fraction of a metre. _____$\frac{3}{10}$_____ m

b) in centimetres. _____30_____ cm

59

Check-up test 1

1 Find the value of $\frac{1}{4}$ of these coins. _____2_____ p

1 mark

2 Tick the container that is about $\frac{3}{4}$ full.

1 mark

3 A sheet of paper is cut into four equal pieces.
What fraction of the whole sheet is three pieces? _____$\frac{3}{4}$_____

1 mark

4 How many quarters are equal to one-half? _____2_____ quarters

1 mark

5 True or false? Three-quarters is purple.   True ☐   False ✓

1 mark

6 Draw a cross on the line to show $2\frac{1}{4}$.

1   ✳   2   3

1 mark

7 How many pence is half of £1? _____50_____ p

1 mark

8 Write the answer to 1 ÷ 2 as a fraction. _____$\frac{1}{2}$_____

1 mark

9 True or false? $\frac{1}{3}$ of a shape is smaller than $\frac{1}{2}$ of the shape.

True ✓   False ☐

1 mark

10 One-quarter subtracted from three-quarters is equal to how many halves?
_____1_____ halves

1 mark

11 An orange is cut into six equal pieces. What fraction of the orange is one piece?

$\frac{1}{6}$

☐ 1 mark

12 Tick the circle that has about $\frac{1}{5}$ shaded.

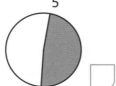 ☐ 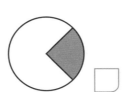 ☐  ☐   ✓

☐ 1 mark

13 A 1m plank of wood is cut into eight equal lengths.

What fraction of a metre is each length? ___$\frac{1}{8}$___ m

☐ 1 mark

14 True or false? $\frac{1}{3}$ is larger than $\frac{1}{6}$.

True ✓   False ☐

☐ 1 mark

15 Two cups are the same size. Cup A is $\frac{1}{5}$ full. Cup B is $\frac{1}{7}$ full.

Which cup contains more? ___A___

☐ 1 mark

16 A bag contains 20 nuts. Jon has $\frac{1}{10}$ of them, Dan has $\frac{1}{2}$ of them and Mia has $\frac{1}{5}$ of them.

a) Who has the most nuts? ___Dan___

b) How many more nuts does Mia have than Jon? ___2___

☐ 1 mark

17 Find $\frac{1}{6}$ of 30cm. ___5___ cm

☐ 1 mark

18 What is one-fifth of 20? ___4___

☐ 1 mark

19 How many minutes is $\frac{1}{10}$ of an hour? ___6___ min

☐ 1 mark

20 A 3m length of tinsel is cut into 4 equal pieces. Write the length of each piece:

a) as a fraction of a metre. ___$\frac{3}{4}$___ m

b) in centimetres. ___75___ cm

☐ 1 mark

Total

☐

20 marks

61

Understand non-unit fractions as areas of shapes

Key point

Unit fractions have the numerator **1**, for example, $\frac{1}{5}$.

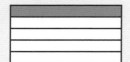

$\frac{1}{5}$ is **1 part of a whole** when a whole is split into **5 equal parts**.

When the **numerator** is **not 1**, the fraction means several parts of a whole.
The **numerator** (the top number) shows how many parts are being described.

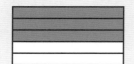

$\frac{3}{5}$ is **3 parts of a whole** when a whole is split into **5 equal parts**.

Get started

1 What fraction of this shape is purple?

$\frac{2}{3}$

2 Colour three-quarters of this shape.

3 True or false? Three-eighths are purple.

True ☐

False ✓

4 Write $\frac{3}{5}$ in words. ___three-fifths___

5 Which shape is $\frac{2}{3}$ purple?

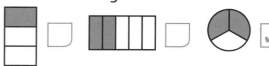 ✓

6 Write sixth-sevenths in digits. $\frac{6}{7}$

7 Colour five-ninths of this shape.

8 Write the numerator of four-fifths.

4

Now try these

9 A loaf of bread is cut into six equal slices.
What fraction of the whole loaf is five slices? $\frac{5}{6}$

10 Tick the shape that is $\frac{2}{5}$ purple.

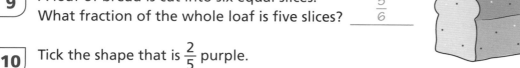

11 A block of cheese is cut into eight equal slices. Luke eats five of the slices.

What fraction of the whole cheese does he eat? $\frac{5}{8}$

12 A rope is cut into seven equal lengths.

What fraction of the whole rope is five of the lengths? ___$\frac{5}{7}$___

13 A chocolate bar has 8 chunks. Dev eats $\frac{3}{8}$ of the bar.

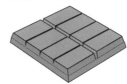

What fraction of the bar is left? ___$\frac{5}{8}$___

14 Five girls each eat one-sixth of a pie. What fraction is left over? ___$\frac{1}{6}$___

15 What fraction of the cylinder is purple?

___$\frac{3}{5}$___

16 True or false? $\frac{1}{4} + \frac{1}{4} + \frac{1}{4} = \frac{3}{4}$ True ☑   False ☐

Challenge

17 A patio is made from nine square tiles, all the same size. One tile is black and the rest are white.

What fraction of the patio is white? ___$\frac{8}{9}$___

18 Cross out the pattern that does not show $\frac{3}{6}$ purple.

19 Colour parts of this shape to show $\frac{7}{9}$.

20 To what number will the arrow point after $\frac{3}{8}$ of a turn clockwise?

___7___

21 A rug is $\frac{1}{8}$ red, $\frac{3}{8}$ yellow, $\frac{3}{8}$ white and the rest is orange. What fraction is orange? ___$\frac{1}{8}$___

22 How many ninths more than $\frac{1}{9}$ is $\frac{5}{9}$? ___4___ ninths

23 | $\frac{3}{7}$ | $\frac{1}{7}$ | $\frac{6}{7}$ | $\frac{4}{7}$ |

Look at the fractions above. Which of these fractions is:

a) the largest? ___$\frac{6}{7}$___ **b)** the smallest? ___$\frac{1}{7}$___

24 The minute hand of this clock turns $\frac{2}{3}$ of a full turn from the top.

What number will it be pointing to? ___8___

Recognise tenths and count in tenths

Key point

When something is divided into 10 equal parts each part is called a **tenth**.

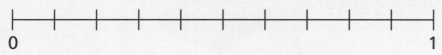

0   1

When counting in tenths, every tenth number will be a whole number.

$0, \dfrac{1}{10}, \dfrac{2}{10}, \dfrac{3}{10}, \dfrac{4}{10}, \dfrac{5}{10}, \dfrac{6}{10}, \dfrac{7}{10}, \dfrac{8}{10}, \dfrac{9}{10}, 1, ...$

When continuing this sequence remember that $\dfrac{10}{10}$ and **1** have the same value.

$1, 1\dfrac{1}{10}, 1\dfrac{2}{10}, 1\dfrac{3}{10}, 1\dfrac{4}{10} ...$ or $\dfrac{10}{10}, \dfrac{11}{10}, \dfrac{12}{10}, \dfrac{13}{10}, \dfrac{14}{10} ...$ Both are correct.

Get started

1 How many tenths of the whole are purple?

_____4_____ tenths

2 Write what number the arrow is pointing to.

$\dfrac{7}{10}$

0   ↑   1

3 What is one-tenth more than $\dfrac{8}{10}$?

$\dfrac{9}{10}$

4 What is two-tenths less than one whole?

$\dfrac{8}{10}$

5 Which number is missing from this sequence?

$\dfrac{8}{10}, \underline{\dfrac{9}{10}}, 1, 1\dfrac{1}{10}, 1\dfrac{2}{10}$

6 How many tenths of a metre make a whole metre?

_____10_____ tenths

7 Write the next number in the sequence.

$3\dfrac{4}{10}, 3\dfrac{5}{10}, 3\dfrac{6}{10}, 3\dfrac{7}{10}, \underline{3\dfrac{8}{10}}$

8 Colour three more tenths of this circle.

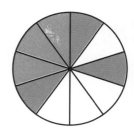

Now try these

9 One-tenth of a kilogram of sand and $\dfrac{6}{10}$ of a kilogram of cement are put into a bucket. What fraction of a kilogram does the mixture weigh? _____$\dfrac{7}{10}$_____ kg

10 What is $2\dfrac{9}{10} + \dfrac{1}{10}$? _____3_____

11 Colour squares so that half of this grid is coloured.
How many tenths are now coloured? ___5___ tenths

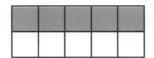

12 How many tenths are in two whole ones? ___20___ tenths

13 Write the missing number.

$$\frac{12}{10} = 1\boxed{\frac{2}{10}}$$

14 Write the missing number to give the mass shown.

$8\boxed{\frac{3}{10}}$ kg

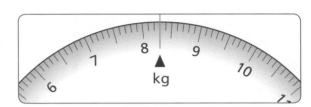

15 How many centimetres in one-tenth of a metre? ___10___ cm

16 Count back six-tenths from 5. What number do you reach? ___$4\frac{4}{10}$___

Challenge

17 What is the difference between one whole and three-tenths? ___$\frac{7}{10}$___

18 Some square carpet tiles have sides that are each $\frac{1}{10}$ of a metre.

How long is a line of 13 touching tiles, in metres? ___$1\frac{3}{10}$___ m

19 Write the missing fractions in this sequence.

$\frac{15}{10}$, ___$\frac{14}{10}$___ , $\frac{13}{10}$, $\frac{12}{10}$, ___$\frac{11}{10}$___ , 1

20 True or false? $\frac{5}{10}$ is equal to $\frac{1}{2}$.   True ☑   False ☐

21 If $\frac{1}{10}$ litre of water flows out of a tap every second,
how many litres will flow out in 20 seconds?

___2___ l

22 A line is divided into 10 equal parts.
If nine of the parts measure 9cm in total, what is the length of the whole line? ___10___ cm

23 Erin ran a race in $10\frac{1}{2}$ seconds. Kelly took four-tenths of a second longer.

How long did Kelly take? ___$10\frac{9}{10}$___ sec

24 How many tenths greater than $3\frac{1}{2}$ is 5? ___15___ tenths

Recognise that tenths arise from dividing by 10

Key point

When 1 pie is shared equally between 10 people, each gets one-tenth.

$1 \div 10 = \frac{1}{10}$

When 2 pies are shared equally between 10 people each gets two-tenths, and so on.

$2 \div 10 = \frac{2}{10}$

$3 \div 10 = \frac{3}{10}$

Get started

1 $4 \div 10 = \dfrac{4}{10}$

2 $7 \div 10 = \dfrac{7}{10}$

3 What is nine divided by ten, as a fraction?

$\dfrac{9}{10}$

4 $\boxed{9} \div 10 = \dfrac{9}{10}$

5 What is 2 melons shared equally between 10, as a fraction? $\dfrac{2}{10}$

6 What number divided by 10 gives $\dfrac{6}{10}$?

6

7 What is the arrow pointing to? $\dfrac{3}{10}$

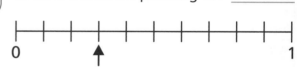

8 Four divided by ten. Write the answer in words.

four-tenths

Now try these

9 If 2 cakes are divided equally between 10 people, what fraction of a cake does each get? $\dfrac{2}{10}$

10 One pot of yoghurt is shared equally into 10 bowls.

What fraction of the pot is in each bowl? $\dfrac{1}{10}$

11 An 8m rope is cut into 10 equal lengths. What fraction of a metre is each length? $\dfrac{8}{10}$ m

12 A machine makes 10 nails from a piece of metal weighing
9g. What is the weight of each nail as a fraction of a gram? $\frac{9}{10}$ g

13 Dad poured three litres of lemonade equally into 10 cups. How much is there in each cup?

Give your answer as a fraction of a litre. $\frac{3}{10}$ l

14 These five bars of chocolate are split equally between 10 people.

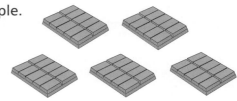

a) How many chunks does each get? _____5_____

b) What fraction of a bar is this? $\frac{1}{2}$ or $\frac{5}{10}$

15 Tick which is larger. 3 ÷ 10 ✓ $\frac{2}{10}$ ☐

16 10 sticks are laid touching in a line. Each stick is $\frac{7}{10}$ m long.

What is the length of the line? _____7_____ m

Challenge

17 True or false? 10 lots of $\frac{3}{10}$ is 3 wholes.   True ✓   False ☐

18 A line of 10 squares measures 5m.
How long is each square, as a fraction of a metre? $\frac{5}{10}$ or $\frac{1}{2}$ m

19 10 identical boots weigh 4kg in total.
As a fraction of a kilogram, what does one boot weigh? $\frac{4}{10}$ kg

20 As he walks, each of Dominic's steps is $\frac{7}{10}$ m apart.
If he takes 10 steps, how far from the start has he walked? _____7_____ m

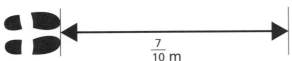

$\frac{7}{10}$ m

21 Divide five by ten. Circle two correct answers. $\frac{1}{5}$ $\frac{10}{5}$ $\boxed{\frac{5}{10}}$ $\frac{1}{10}$ $\boxed{\frac{1}{2}}$

22 A bag of sugar is 2kg. Each jar holds $\frac{2}{10}$ kg of sugar.

How many jars are needed for all the sugar? _____10_____

23 Luke walks from home to work and back again each day
for 5 days. He walks 8km in total. What is the distance
from his home to his work, as a fraction of a kilometre? $\frac{8}{10}$ km

24 The digit after a decimal point shows the number of tenths, for example, 0.2 = $\frac{2}{10}$.

Write 0.4 as a fraction. $\frac{4}{10}$

Use fractions as numbers on a number line

Key point

Each whole number on a line can be split into parts and described using fractions.

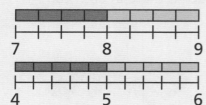

Here each whole is split into **quarters**.

Here each whole is split into **fifths**.

A whole number and a fraction can be used to show points on the line, for example:

$7\frac{1}{4}, 8\frac{3}{4}, 4\frac{3}{5}, 5\frac{4}{5}$ These are called **mixed numbers**.

Get started

1 Write the number shown by the cross on the number line. $4\frac{2}{3}$

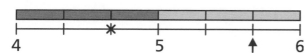

2 Write the number shown by the arrow on the number line above.

$5\frac{2}{3}$

3 How many equal parts is this divided into?

8

4 What is the missing number?

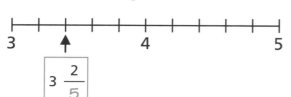

$3\ \dfrac{2}{5}$

5 What is one-fifth less than 5 wholes?

$4\frac{4}{5}$

6 Which number is missing from this sequence?

$0, \frac{1}{5}, \frac{2}{5}, \frac{3}{5}, \frac{4}{5}, 1, \underline{\quad 1\frac{1}{5} \quad}, 1\frac{2}{5}$

7 How many equal parts is each whole on this ruler divided into?

6

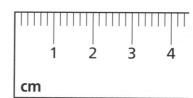

8 What number is the same as five-fifths?

1

Now try these

9 How many packets are shown? $5\frac{3}{4}$

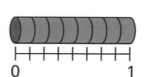

10 What is $\frac{1}{10}$ more than $3\frac{7}{10}$? $3\frac{8}{10}$

11 When counting on in sixths, what number comes after 2? $2\frac{1}{6}$

12 Write the next two numbers in the sequence. 6, $6\frac{1}{4}$, $6\frac{1}{2}$, $6\frac{3}{4}$, ___7___ , ___$7\frac{1}{4}$___

13 How many thirds in two whole ones? ___6___ thirds

14 Count back three-tenths from two. What number do you reach? ___$1\frac{7}{10}$___

15 This ruler shows tenths of a centimetre.

a) Draw a cross to show $\frac{3}{10}$ cm.

b) Draw an arrow to show $1\frac{7}{10}$ cm.

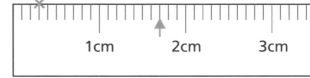

16 How many tenths are there in $2\frac{1}{2}$? ___25___ tenths

Challenge

17 Count back $\frac{2}{3}$ from 4. What number do you reach? ___$3\frac{1}{3}$___

18 What is the difference between $1\frac{1}{5}$ and $1\frac{3}{5}$? ___$\frac{2}{5}$___

19 Count on four-sixths from the arrow on the line. Where do you land? ___$2\frac{3}{6}$ or $2\frac{1}{2}$___

20 What is $7\frac{7}{8} - \frac{4}{8}$? ___$7\frac{3}{8}$___

21 This line is split into twelfths. What is the missing number? $\frac{1}{2} = \frac{6}{12}$

0   1

22 Toby jumps $4\frac{3}{10}$ m in the long jump and Libby jumps $5\frac{3}{10}$ m.

How much further does Libby jump than Toby? ___1___ m

23 True or false? $\frac{1}{4} = \frac{2}{8}$

True ✓   False ☐

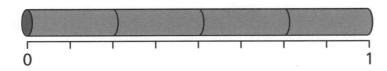

24 How many fifths greater than 8 is 9? ___5___ fifths

Compare fractions with the same denominator

Key point

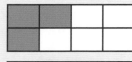

$\frac{3}{8}$ is purple.   The shape is split into **8 equal parts (denominator)** and **3 of the parts are purple (numerator).**

$\frac{5}{8}$ is purple.   The shape is split into **8 equal parts (denominator)** and **5 of the parts are purple (numerator).**

$\frac{3}{8} < \frac{5}{8}$ If the **denominators** are the same, fractions can be compared using just the **numerators**.

Get started

1 True or false? $\frac{5}{8}$ is larger than $\frac{1}{8}$.

True ✓   False ☐

2 Write what fraction of each shape is purple.

a)

$\frac{1}{6}$

b)

$\frac{5}{6}$

3 Which is more? $\frac{1}{6}$ of an apple or $\frac{5}{6}$ of the same apple? _____ $\frac{5}{6}$

4 Circle the larger fraction.   ⬭$\frac{3}{5}$ $\frac{2}{5}$

5 Which letter on the number line shows:

a) $\frac{6}{8}$? _____F_____   b) $\frac{4}{8}$? _____D_____

0   A   B   C   D   E   F   G   1

6 True or false? $\frac{5}{10} < \frac{7}{10}$

True ✓   False ☐

7 Use either the < or > sign to show which fraction is larger.

$\frac{5}{4}$ > $\frac{3}{4}$

8 Is $\frac{3}{4}$ of a kilogram more or less than $\frac{1}{4}$ of a kilogram? _____more_____

Now try these

9 Write the fraction of this shape that is:

a) ⬛ _____$\frac{5}{9}$_____   b) ☐ _____$\frac{4}{9}$_____

c) Which of these two fractions is larger? _____$\frac{5}{9}$_____

10 Tick to show how the fractions in this sequence are ordered: $\frac{1}{5}, \frac{2}{5}, \frac{3}{5}, \frac{4}{5}$

smallest to largest ✓   largest to smallest ☐

11 Mark $\frac{3}{8}$ with a cross and $\frac{7}{8}$ with an arrow on this line.   0 ⌐   ✗   ⭡   1

12 Circle the fraction that is larger than one-half. $\frac{1}{8}$ $\frac{3}{8}$ $\boxed{\frac{7}{8}}$

13 Three jugs are the same size. Jug A is $\frac{6}{10}$ full. Jug B is $\frac{7}{10}$ full. Jug C is $\frac{10}{10}$ full.
Which jug contains most? _____C_____

14 Cross out one of these fractions so that the rest are in order of size. $\frac{3}{10}$ $\frac{4}{10}$ $\frac{6}{10}$ $\cancel{\frac{2}{10}}$ $\frac{9}{10}$

15 Write these fractions from smallest to largest: $\frac{6}{7}$ $\frac{1}{7}$ $\frac{4}{7}$ $\boxed{\frac{1}{7}}$ $\boxed{\frac{4}{7}}$ $\boxed{\frac{6}{7}}$

16 A banana was cut into 9 equal pieces.
Natasha ate $\frac{4}{9}$ of it and Beata ate the rest. Who ate more? _____Beata_____

Challenge

17 Holly mixed some paint. She used $\frac{3}{8}$l of red paint, $\frac{3}{8}$l of blue paint and $\frac{2}{8}$l of purple paint. Tick the statement that is true. She used:

a) more blue than red. ☐   b) more purple than red. ☐   c) more red than purple. ☑

18 Write these fractions from smallest to largest: $\frac{4}{9}$ $\frac{2}{9}$ $\frac{5}{9}$ $\frac{3}{9}$ $\boxed{\frac{2}{9}}$ $\boxed{\frac{3}{9}}$ $\boxed{\frac{4}{9}}$ $\boxed{\frac{5}{9}}$

19 Liam says that, because $\frac{4}{8} = \frac{1}{2}$, then $\frac{1}{2} < \frac{5}{8}$.

Is he correct?   Yes ☑   No ☐

20 Each whole is split into 5 equal parts on a number line.
Crosses are marked at three points: $\frac{4}{5}$, $1\frac{1}{5}$ and $\frac{2}{5}$.
Write these numbers from smallest to largest. $\frac{2}{5}$ $\frac{4}{5}$ $1\frac{1}{5}$

21 A set contains 12 cards. Connor has $\frac{5}{12}$ of them, Marta has $\frac{4}{12}$ of them and Jamie has the rest of them.

a) Who has the most cards? _____Connor_____   b) How many cards has Jamie? ___3___

22 True or false? The largest fraction here plus the smallest fraction is equal to one whole.
$\frac{3}{6}$ $\frac{5}{6}$ $\frac{2}{6}$ $\frac{1}{6}$ $\frac{4}{6}$ True ☑   False ☐

23 Jessica says that $\frac{4}{5}$ of an amount of money is always larger than $\frac{1}{5}$ of a different amount of money. Is she correct?   Yes ☐   No ☑

24 Find $\frac{1}{5}$ of 30p and $\frac{4}{5}$ of 5p.

Write which is larger. $\frac{1}{5}$ of 30p = 6p

Recognise fractions of a set of objects

Key point

To find fractions of sets of objects, arrange them into **equal groups**.

To find **one-fifth** of these 10 faces, group them into **5 groups**.

$\frac{1}{5}$ (1 group) of the **10** faces is **2** faces.

$\frac{3}{5}$ (3 groups) of the **10** faces is **6** faces.

Get started

1 True or false? The 3 purple faces are $\frac{1}{4}$ of all the faces.

True ✓

False ☐

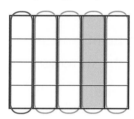

2 What fraction of the cubes are purple?

$\frac{1}{5}$

3 Colour some more cubes above so that now $\frac{3}{5}$ of the cubes are coloured.

4 What fraction of these cats have:

a) collars? $\frac{1}{3}$

b) no collars? $\frac{2}{3}$

5 Draw more loops on this grid to show 5 equal groups.

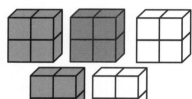

6 Now colour $\frac{1}{5}$ of the squares in the grid above.

7 Draw more loops on this grid to show quarters.

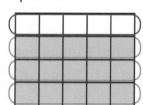

8 Now colour $\frac{3}{4}$ of the squares in the grid above.

Now try these

9 Draw loops around the sweets to split them equally into three groups.

10 How many is one-third of the 6 sweets? __2__

11 12 grapes are arranged into 6 equal groups. How many is $\frac{1}{6}$ of the 12 grapes? __2__

12 | Tick which tile pattern shows $\frac{1}{6}$ purple.

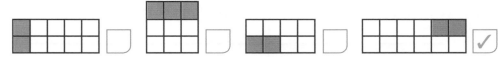

13 | How many equal groups are some objects sorted into to show eighths? ___8___

14 | There are 16 beads on this necklace.

Colour $\frac{1}{8}$ of the beads.

Draw crosses on $\frac{3}{8}$ of the beads.

15 | What fraction of these 8 balls are white?

$\frac{3}{8}$

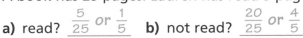

16 | What fraction of these 24 balls are white?

$\frac{3}{8}$

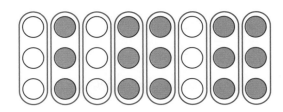

Challenge

17 | A book has 25 pages. Lauren has read 5 pages. What fraction of the book has she:

a) read? $\frac{5}{25}$ or $\frac{1}{5}$ **b)** not read? $\frac{20}{25}$ or $\frac{4}{5}$

18 | Colour $\frac{5}{6}$ of the 24 squares in this grid.

19 | How many is $\frac{5}{6}$ of 24? ___20___

20 | What is one-third of 30 sheep? ___10___

21 | A bag contains 2 red apples, 6 yellow apples and 8 green apples. What fraction of the apples are:

a) red? $\frac{2}{16}$ or $\frac{1}{8}$ **b)** green? $\frac{8}{16}$ or $\frac{1}{2}$

22 | Write the fraction of stars that are white.

a)  $\frac{2}{6}$ **b)** $\frac{1}{3}$

23 | Zain has £1 in 1p coins. He sorts the coins into 10 equal piles. What is the value of the coins in:

a) one pile? ___10___ p   **b)** three piles? ___30___ p

24 | What is $\frac{3}{10}$ of £1? ___30___ p

Check-up test 2

1 What fraction of the shape is purple? $\frac{2}{5}$

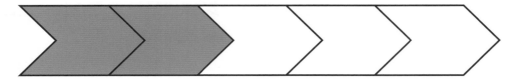

2 Write $\frac{3}{8}$ in words. _three-eighths_

3 Six boys each take one-seventh of a pitta bread.

What fraction is left over? $\frac{1}{7}$

4 $\frac{5}{9}$ $\frac{1}{9}$ $\frac{4}{9}$ $\frac{2}{9}$

Look at the fractions above. Which is:

a) the largest? $\frac{5}{9}$ **b)** the smallest? $\frac{1}{9}$

5 What is six-tenths less than one whole? $\frac{4}{10}$

6 Colour six more tenths of this circle.

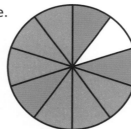

7 What is $2\frac{3}{10} + \frac{1}{10}$? $2\frac{4}{10}$

8 True or false? $\frac{5}{10}$ is equal to $\frac{1}{2}$. True ✓ False ☐

9 What is seven divided by ten, as a fraction? $\frac{7}{10}$

10 A bag of rice is 3kg. Each jar holds $\frac{3}{10}$ kg of rice.

How many jars are needed for all the rice? _10_

11 Write the number shown by the arrow. ___$5\frac{1}{3}$___

1 mark

12 What is $\frac{1}{10}$ more than $2\frac{3}{10}$? ___$2\frac{4}{10}$___

1 mark

13 What is the difference between $1\frac{4}{5}$ and $1\frac{3}{5}$? ___$\frac{1}{5}$___

1 mark

14 Circle the larger fraction. $\frac{4}{7}$ $\boxed{\frac{6}{7}}$

1 mark

15 Circle the fraction that is larger than one-half. $\frac{2}{6}$ $\frac{1}{6}$ $\boxed{\frac{4}{6}}$

1 mark

16 Adam says that $\frac{3}{4}$ of an amount of money is always larger than $\frac{1}{4}$ of a different amount of money. Is he correct?

Yes ☐   No ☑

1 mark

17 What fraction of the cubes are purple? ___$\frac{2}{5}$ or $\frac{8}{20}$___

1 mark

18 How many is one-fifth of 10 ice creams? ___2___

1 mark

19 What fraction of these 8 frogs are jumping? ___$\frac{3}{8}$___

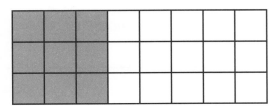

1 mark

20 Colour $\frac{3}{8}$ of the 24 squares in this grid.

1 mark

Total

☐

20 marks

Use non-unit fractions in a variety of representations

Key point

Fractions involve a **whole** being split into **equal parts**. Here different wholes are all split into 5 equal parts. Each part is one-fifth.

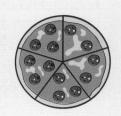

Get started

1 What fraction of these flags are white?

$\frac{2}{7}$

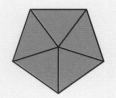

2 Tick the shape that is $\frac{4}{6}$ purple.

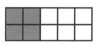

3 Circle the fraction made when three wholes are divided by 10. $\frac{10}{3}$ $\frac{1}{3}$ $\left(\frac{3}{10}\right)$

4 Colour five-twelfths of this shape.

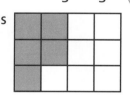

5 What is one-fifth of 15? _____ 3 _____

6 Draw a cross at $\frac{3}{4}$ on this line.

0   1

7 What fraction of the cubes are purple?

$\frac{5}{6}$ or $\frac{20}{24}$

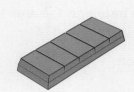

8 One whole pound is split into tenths.

How much is one-tenth? _____ 10 _____ p

Now try these

9 A cake is cut into six equal slices. What fraction of the whole cake is five slices? _____ $\frac{5}{6}$

10 If A stands for $\frac{1}{5}$, what does B stand for? _____ $\frac{2}{5}$

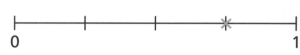
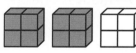

11 Draw a cross on the line above to show four-fifths.

12 True or false? $\frac{1}{5} + \frac{1}{5} + \frac{1}{5} = \frac{3}{5}$ True ✓   False ☐

13 Which letter on the number line shows $\frac{5}{8}$? ___E___

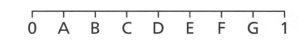

0   A   B   C   D   E   F   G   1

14 What fraction does C represent on the number line above? ___$\frac{3}{8}$___

15 There are 4 yellow tennis balls and 3 green ones.

What fraction of the balls are green? ___$\frac{3}{7}$___

16 A piece of string is cut into eight equal lengths.
What fraction of the whole piece of string are three of the lengths together? ___$\frac{3}{8}$___

Challenge

17 What fraction of a week is: **a)** one day? ___$\frac{1}{7}$___   **b)** two days? ___$\frac{2}{7}$___

18 A group of 10 children get into pairs.
What fraction of the group is:

a) one pair? ___$\frac{1}{5}$ or $\frac{2}{10}$___

b) four pairs? ___$\frac{4}{5}$ or $\frac{8}{10}$___

19 Jonah eats $\frac{3}{10}$ of a chocolate bar. What fraction is left? ___$\frac{7}{10}$___

20 What fraction do you get if you divide eight by ten?

Write the answer in words. ___eight-tenths___

21 Colour $\frac{5}{6}$ of the 18 squares in this grid.

22 How many times as long as $\frac{1}{10}$ of a kilometre is $\frac{3}{10}$ of a kilometre? ___3___

23

$\frac{3}{7}$	$\frac{1}{7}$	$\frac{6}{7}$	$\frac{4}{7}$

Look at the fractions above. Which of these fractions is:

a) the largest? ___$\frac{6}{7}$___   **b)** the smallest? ___$\frac{1}{7}$___

24 One-third of Macy's money is 10p.

a) How much is $\frac{2}{3}$ of her money? ___20___ p

b) How much is the whole amount of her money? ___30___ p

Recognise fractions showing the same amount

Key point

Parts of these two shapes are purple and white.

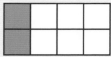

The first shape is $\frac{1}{4}$ purple and $\frac{3}{4}$ white.

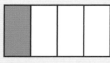

The second shape is $\frac{2}{8}$ purple and $\frac{6}{8}$ white.

The same amount of each shape is purple. $\frac{1}{4}$ is the same amount as $\frac{2}{8}$.

The same amount of each shape is white. $\frac{3}{4}$ is the same amount as $\frac{6}{8}$.

Get started

1 Do these two shapes show the same amount purple?

Yes ☑   No ☐

2 How many quarters are the same as one-half? ___2___ quarters

3 Do these two shapes have the same amount purple?

Yes ☑   No ☐

4 One-half is the same as how many sixths? ___3___ sixths

5 What number is missing?

$\frac{1}{2}$ is the same amount as $\boxed{\dfrac{3}{6}}$.

6 Do these two shapes show the same amount purple?

Yes ☑   No ☐

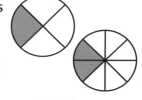

7 $\frac{1}{4}$ is the same amount as $\boxed{\dfrac{2}{8}}$.

8 How many eighths are the same amount as one-half? ___4___ eighths

Now try these

9 Three-quarters is how many eighths? ___6___ eighths

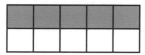

10 How many tenths is the same as one-half?

$\frac{1}{2} = \boxed{\dfrac{5}{10}}$

11 This cylinder is $\frac{3}{6}$ purple. Write another fraction to show what fraction of the cylinder is purple. ___$\frac{1}{2}$___

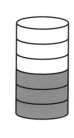

12 Look at the shapes and write the missing numbers.

$\dfrac{1}{3}$ is the same amount as $\dfrac{3}{9}$.

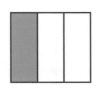

13 A cereal bar has 8 chunks. Kim eats one-quarter of the whole bar.

How many chunks does she eat? ___2___

14 A tart is cut into six equal slices. Aswin's family eat half of the tart.

How many slices do they eat? ___3___

15 David's birthday cake is cut into equal slices.
He eats $\dfrac{2}{8}$ of the cake. Is this more, less or the same as $\dfrac{1}{4}$ of the cake? ___the same___

16 For each diagram, write the fraction of the shape that is purple.

a)

$\dfrac{2}{3}$

b)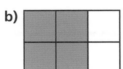

$\dfrac{4}{6}$ or $\dfrac{2}{3}$

c)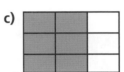

$\dfrac{6}{9}$ or $\dfrac{2}{3}$

Challenge

17 Eight-twelfths is the same
amount as how many thirds? ___2___ thirds

18 A number line shows tenths.
How many tenths are the same as one-half? ___5___ tenths

0   1

19 A number line is split into fifths.
How many tenths are the same as one-fifth? ___2___ tenths

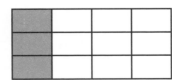

0   1

20 What is the missing number? $\dfrac{4}{5}$ is the same as $\dfrac{8}{10}$.

21 Colour one-quarter of this rectangle.

22 How many twelfths have you coloured above? ___3___ twelfths

23 What fraction of the rectangle above is not coloured? $\dfrac{9}{12} = \dfrac{3}{4}$

24 A wall is covered in tiles. $\dfrac{3}{12}$ of the tiles are white. $\dfrac{1}{4}$ of the tiles are pink.

Are there the same number of white tiles as pink tiles?   Yes ✓   No ☐

Find equivalent fractions using a fraction wall

Key point

Fractions are called **equivalent** when they stand for the **same** amount.

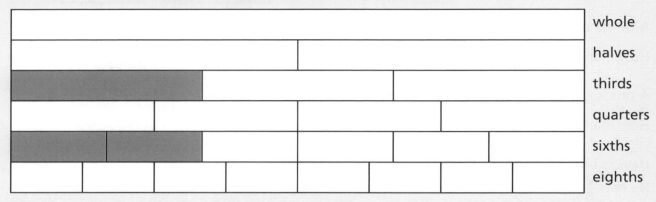

The purple bars show that $\frac{1}{3}$ and $\frac{2}{6}$ are **equivalent**.

Get started

1 Use the fraction wall to help you find how many quarters are equivalent to one-half. ___2___ quarters

2 One-half is equivalent to how many sixths? ___3___ sixths

3 One-quarter is equivalent to how many eighths? ___2___ eighths

4 One-third is equivalent to how many sixths? ___2___ sixths

5 The fraction $\frac{1}{2}$ is equivalent to how many eighths?

___4___ eighths

6 $\frac{1}{4}$ is equivalent to $\dfrac{2}{8}$.

7 $\frac{2}{3}$ is equivalent to $\dfrac{4}{6}$.

8 How many quarters are equivalent to one whole?

___4___ quarters

Now try these

9 One-quarter of this shape is purple. How many eighths is this? ___2___ eighths

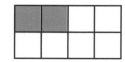

10 Colour one-half of these rectangles.

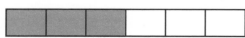

Now write the missing number. $\frac{1}{2} = \dfrac{3}{6}$

11 How many tenths are equivalent to three-fifths? $\frac{3}{5} = \dfrac{6}{10}$

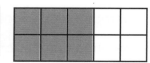

12 Six of these 15 buttons are white. The buttons are grouped into fifths.

How many fifths are white? $\frac{6}{15} = \frac{2}{5}$

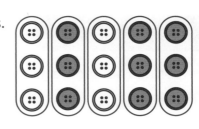

13 Nine of the 15 buttons are purple.

How many fifths are purple? $\frac{9}{15} = \frac{3}{5}$

14 Write a fraction with the denominator 9 that is equivalent to $\frac{1}{3}$.

$\frac{1}{3} = \frac{3}{9}$

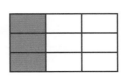

15 There are 16 beads on this necklace. Colour 8 of the beads. Write two equivalent fractions to show what fraction of the beads are coloured in. $\frac{8}{16}$ $\frac{1}{2}$

16 Now draw crosses on 4 of the beads. Write two equivalent fractions to show what fraction of the beads have crosses. $\frac{4}{16}$ $\frac{1}{4}$

Challenge

17 One-fifth of the grid is purple. $\frac{1}{5} = \frac{2}{10}$

18 Four-fifths of the grid is white. $\frac{4}{5} = \frac{8}{10}$

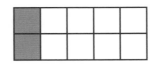

19 Some friends share a birthday cake. Olivia has $\frac{2}{8}$ of it. Brooke has $\frac{1}{4}$ of it.

Do they have the same amount?   Yes ✓   No ☐

20 What is the missing numerator? $\frac{3}{4} = \frac{6}{8}$

21 For each diagram, write the fraction of bow ties that are white.

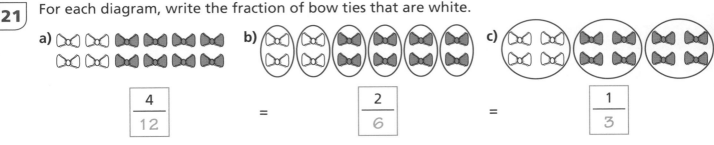

a) $\frac{4}{12}$ = b) $\frac{2}{6}$ = c) $\frac{1}{3}$

22 What fraction of each set of bow ties above are purple?   a) $\frac{8}{12}$ b) $\frac{4}{6}$ c) $\frac{2}{3}$

23 Complete this pattern. $\frac{1}{2} = \frac{2}{4} = \frac{4}{8}$

24 Two of these fractions are equivalent to one-half. Circle them. $\frac{2}{3}$ $\boxed{\frac{5}{10}}$ $\frac{3}{8}$ $\frac{4}{4}$ $\frac{4}{6}$ $\boxed{\frac{6}{12}}$

Add fractions with the same denominator

Key point

When adding fractions ask: *'Are the denominators the same?'*

If so, **add the numerators only**. Use the **same denominator**.

numerator ⟶ $\dfrac{3}{10} + \dfrac{6}{10} = \dfrac{9}{10}$
denominator ⟶

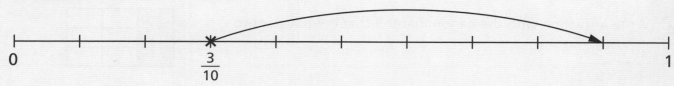

Get started

1 $\dfrac{2}{7} + \dfrac{3}{7} = \boxed{\dfrac{5}{7}}$

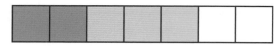

2 $\dfrac{1}{10} + \dfrac{6}{10} = \boxed{\dfrac{7}{10}}$

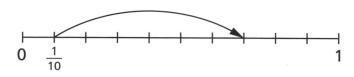

3 $\dfrac{1}{8}$ plus $\dfrac{4}{8} = \boxed{\dfrac{5}{8}}$

4 Add $\dfrac{1}{3}$ and $\dfrac{1}{3}$. $\quad\dfrac{2}{3}$

5 $\boxed{\dfrac{5}{9}} + \dfrac{3}{9} = \dfrac{8}{9}$

6 Double $\dfrac{2}{5}$. $\quad\dfrac{4}{5}$

7 $\dfrac{1}{8} + \dfrac{1}{8} + \dfrac{3}{8} = \boxed{\dfrac{5}{8}}$

8 $\dfrac{4}{12} + \boxed{\dfrac{7}{12}} = \dfrac{11}{12}$

Now try these

9 Write the fraction of this shape that is:

a) $\quad\dfrac{5}{12}$ b) $\quad\dfrac{6}{12}$ c) or $\quad\dfrac{11}{12}$

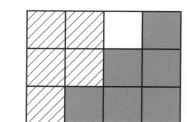

10 Count on $\dfrac{4}{6}$ from $\dfrac{1}{6}$. $\quad\dfrac{5}{6}$

11 What is added to $\dfrac{1}{11}$ to get $\dfrac{9}{11}$? $\quad\dfrac{8}{11}$

12 Increase five-sevenths by one-seventh. $\frac{6}{7}$

13 What is $\frac{2}{9}$ more than $\frac{5}{9}$? $\frac{7}{9}$

14 Find the sum of four-ninths and three-ninths. $\frac{7}{9}$

15 Find the total of $\frac{2}{6}$ and $\frac{3}{6}$. $\frac{5}{6}$

16 Give the sum of $\frac{5}{12}$ and $\frac{7}{12}$ as a whole number. 1

Challenge

17 $\frac{1}{10}$ m is added to $\frac{6}{10}$ m. What fraction of a metre is still required to make 1 metre? $\frac{3}{10}$ m

18 Find the values of a and b.

$\frac{1}{10} + \frac{4}{10} = \frac{a}{10} = \frac{1}{b}$ $a =$ 5 $b =$ 2

19 Amina mixes one-quarter of a kilogram of sugar with two-quarters of a kilogram of flour.

How many grams is the total mixture? 750 g

20 How many quarters are equivalent to the sum of $\frac{1}{8}$, $\frac{3}{8}$ and $\frac{2}{8}$? 3 quarters

21 A line is 0.4cm. What is the length of another line that is three-tenths of a centimetre longer? Give your answer as a fraction. $\frac{7}{10}$ cm

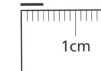

1cm

22 Ollie spent $\frac{1}{6}$ of an hour watching a cartoon and $\frac{2}{6}$ of an hour watching a quiz show.

a) For what fraction of an hour did he watch altogether? $\frac{3}{6}$ or $\frac{1}{2}$ hr

b) How many minutes is this? 30 min

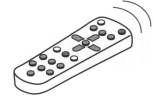

23 Write the answer to $\frac{1}{12} + \frac{5}{12}$ as a fraction with the numerator 1. $\frac{1}{2}$

24 Which two different fractions with the denominator 10 have a total that is equivalent to two-fifths?

$\frac{1}{10} + \frac{3}{10} = \frac{2}{5}$

Subtract fractions with the same denominator

Key point

When subtracting fractions ask: *'Are the denominators the same?'*

If so, **subtract the numerators only**. Use the **same denominator**.

numerator $\longrightarrow$
denominator $\longrightarrow$ $\dfrac{9}{10} - \dfrac{6}{10} = \dfrac{3}{10}$

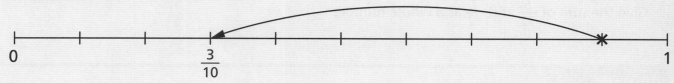

0                    $\dfrac{3}{10}$ 1

Get started

1 $\dfrac{6}{7} - \dfrac{3}{7} = \boxed{\dfrac{3}{7}}$

2 $\dfrac{8}{10} - \dfrac{1}{10} = \boxed{\dfrac{7}{10}}$

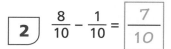

0                              $\dfrac{8}{10}$ 1

3 $\dfrac{7}{8}$ minus $\dfrac{4}{8} = \boxed{\dfrac{3}{8}}$

4 Subtract $\dfrac{1}{3}$ from $\dfrac{2}{3}$. $\dfrac{1}{3}$

5 $\boxed{\dfrac{5}{9}} - \dfrac{3}{9} = \dfrac{2}{9}$

6 $\dfrac{8}{8} - \dfrac{1}{8} = \boxed{\dfrac{7}{8}}$

7 Take $\dfrac{2}{5}$ from one whole. $\dfrac{3}{5}$

8 $\dfrac{9}{12} - \boxed{\dfrac{7}{12}} = \dfrac{2}{12}$

Now try these

9 Decrease five-sevenths by one-seventh. $\dfrac{4}{7}$

10 Count back $\dfrac{4}{6}$ from $\dfrac{5}{6}$. $\dfrac{1}{6}$

11 What is subtracted from $\dfrac{9}{11}$ to get $\dfrac{1}{11}$? $\dfrac{8}{11}$

12 What is $\dfrac{5}{5}$ minus $\dfrac{2}{5}$?

$\dfrac{3}{5}$

13 What is $\frac{2}{9}$ less than $\frac{7}{9}$? _____ $\frac{5}{9}$

14 Find the difference between four-ninths and three-ninths. _____ $\frac{1}{9}$

15 A bag of flour weighs $\frac{8}{10}$ kg. Kyle uses $\frac{3}{10}$ kg of the flour to make a cake.

    a) What fraction of a kilogram is left? _____ $\frac{5}{10}$ or $\frac{1}{2}$ kg

    b) How many grams is this? ___500___ g

16 Zoë walks $\frac{3}{8}$ of the way to school. What fraction is left to walk? _____ $\frac{5}{8}$

Challenge

17 Maria spent $\frac{7}{12}$ of an hour listening to music. For $\frac{1}{12}$ of an hour she listened to hip hop and for the rest of the time she listened to jazz.

    a) For what fraction of an hour did she listen to jazz? _____ $\frac{6}{12}$ or $\frac{1}{2}$ hr

    b) How many minutes is this? ___30___ min

18 Find the values of a and b.

    $\frac{9}{10} - \frac{7}{10} = \frac{a}{10} = \frac{1}{b}$ $a =$ ___2___ $b =$ ___5___

19 Write the answer to $\frac{11}{12} - \frac{5}{12}$ as a fraction with the numerator 1. _____ $\frac{1}{2}$

20 A lorry driver has to travel from one city to another. He drives $\frac{3}{9}$ of the distance before lunch and finishes his journey after lunch.

    a) What fraction of the way does he drive after lunch? _____ $\frac{6}{9}$

    b) How many thirds of the distance is this? ___2___ thirds

21 $\frac{3}{6}$ $\frac{5}{6}$ $\frac{2}{6}$ $\frac{1}{6}$ $\frac{4}{6}$

    What is the largest fraction minus the smallest fraction? _____ $\frac{4}{6}$ or $\frac{2}{3}$

22 A line is 0.4 cm. What is the length of another line that is three-tenths of a centimetre shorter? Give your answer as a fraction. _____ $\frac{1}{10}$ cm

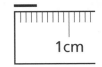

1cm

23 Only $\frac{7}{12}$ of the seats for a football match were sold.

    Some of the seats were sold to women, $\frac{4}{12}$ were sold to men and $\frac{2}{12}$ to children.

    What fraction of the seats were sold to women? _____ $\frac{1}{12}$

24 $1 - \frac{3}{7} + \frac{2}{7} - \frac{4}{7} = \boxed{\dfrac{2}{7}}$

Solve problems with measures

Key point

Fractions can be used to show parts of a whole **unit of measurement** such as a kilogram, a metre, a litre or a centimetre.

For example: $\frac{1}{4}$ kg or $\frac{3}{10}$ cm

Whole numbers and fractions can be used together (as **mixed numbers**) to show measurements **larger than one unit**.

For example: $3\frac{1}{2}$ kg or $5\frac{7}{10}$ cm

When using tenths, a **decimal** can be used.

For example: $5\frac{7}{10}$ cm = 5.7cm

Get started

1 Write two and three-quarter centimetres in digits. _____ $2\frac{3}{4}$ _____ cm

2 Write this measurement in words: $6\frac{1}{2}$ kg.

_____ *six and a half kilograms* _____

3 How many quarters of a kilogram are in 2 kilograms?

_____ *8* _____ quarters

4 Write two-fifths of a metre in digits.

_____ $\frac{2}{5}$ _____ m

5 What length is $\frac{3}{8}$ m more than 3m?

_____ $3\frac{3}{8}$ _____ m

6 What capacity is $\frac{1}{4}$ litre more than 4 litres? _____ $4\frac{1}{4}$ _____ l

7 True or false? $\frac{3}{6}$ litre = $\frac{1}{2}$ litre

True ✓   False ☐

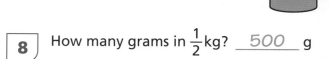

8 How many grams in $\frac{1}{2}$ kg? _____ *500* _____ g

Now try these

9 This line is 0.7cm.
Write its length as a fraction of a centimetre. _____ $\frac{7}{10}$ _____ cm

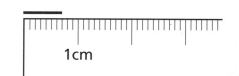

1cm

10 How many tenths of a centimetre make half a centimetre? _____ *5* _____ tenths

11 A metre is divided into 10 equal parts. How many centimetres is the same as $\frac{3}{10}$ m? _____ *30* _____ cm

12 How many minutes is:

a) $\frac{1}{4}$ hour? ___15___ min   b) $\frac{1}{2}$ hour? ___30___ min   c) $1\frac{1}{2}$ hours? ___90___ min

13 What length of time is $\frac{1}{4}$ hour plus $1\frac{1}{4}$ hours? ___$1\frac{1}{2}$___ hr

14 A 1m plank of wood is sawn into six equal lengths.

What fraction of a metre is each length? ___$\frac{1}{6}$___ m

15 A tap pours $\frac{1}{10}$ litre of water every second.

How many litres will it pour in 60 seconds? ___6___ l

16 Write five-tenths of a centimetre as a decimal. ___0.5___ cm

Challenge

17 Circle the heaviest mass. $4\frac{5}{8}$ kg $3\frac{1}{3}$ kg   ⟮$4\frac{7}{8}$ kg⟯

18 Find the difference in grams between $\frac{1}{4}$ of 32g and $\frac{1}{8}$ of 48g. ___2___ g

19 As he walks, each of Omar's steps is $\frac{1}{4}$m apart.

If he takes 9 steps, how far from the start has he walked? ___$2\frac{1}{4}$___ m

$\frac{1}{4}$ m

20 What is one-eighth of a litre less than 2 litres? ___$1\frac{7}{8}$___ l

21 The length of a rectangle is 9cm. Its width is $\frac{1}{3}$ of its length.

Find the perimeter of the rectangle. ___24___ cm

22 Some square cards have sides that are each $\frac{1}{10}$ of a metre.

How long is a line of 19 touching cards, in metres? ___$1\frac{9}{10}$___ m

23 Lily ran a race in $10\frac{1}{2}$ seconds.

Keira took two-tenths of a second longer.

How long did Keira take? ___$10\frac{7}{10}$___ sec

24 How many centimetres less than 1 metre is nine-tenths of a metre? ___10___ cm

Check-up test 3

1 Colour seven-twelfths of this shape.

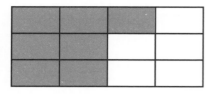

1 mark

2 What is one-sixth of 18? _____3_____

1 mark

3 There are 5 purple socks and 4 white socks.

What fraction of the socks are white? $\frac{4}{9}$

1 mark

4 $\frac{1}{5}$ of Theo's money is 20p.

   a) How much is $\frac{2}{5}$ of his money? _____40_____ p

   b) How much is the whole amount of his money? £ _____1_____

1 mark

5 $\frac{1}{3}$ is the same amount as $\boxed{\dfrac{2}{6}}$.

1 mark

6 A number line shows tenths. How many tenths is the same as one-fifth?

_____2_____ tenths

1 mark

```
|--+--+--+--+--+--+--+--+--+--|
0                             1
```

7 One-half is equivalent to how many eighths? _____4_____ eighths

1 mark

8 Some friends share an orange. Emily has $\frac{3}{12}$. Max has $\frac{1}{3}$ of it.

Do they have the same amount?   Yes ☐   No ☑

1 mark

9 One-quarter is purple. How many twelfths is this?

_____3_____ twelfths

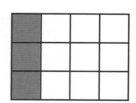

1 mark

10 $\frac{1}{10} + \frac{8}{10} = \boxed{\dfrac{9}{10}}$

1 mark

11 For each diagram, write the fraction of toy cars that are purple.

a)   b)   c)

$$\boxed{\dfrac{8}{12}} \quad = \quad \boxed{\dfrac{4}{6}} \quad = \quad \boxed{\dfrac{2}{3}}$$

1 mark

12 Find the difference between two-sevenths and six-sevenths. ____$\frac{4}{7}$____

1 mark

13 $\frac{1}{10}$ m is added to $\frac{2}{10}$ m.

What fraction of a metre is still required to make 1 metre? ____$\frac{7}{10}$____ m

1 mark

14 Subtract $\frac{1}{5}$ from $\frac{3}{5}$. ____$\frac{2}{5}$____

1 mark

15 Nadia eats $\frac{2}{9}$ of an apple. What fraction is left? ____$\frac{7}{9}$____

1 mark

16 A box of washing powder weighs $\frac{7}{10}$ kg.
Thomas uses $\frac{2}{10}$ kg to do the laundry.

a) What fraction of a kilogram is left? ____$\frac{5}{10}$ or $\frac{1}{2}$____ kg

b) How many grams is this? ____500____ g

1 mark

17 Write this measurement in words: $5\frac{1}{4}$ kg ____five and a quarter kilograms____

1 mark

18 This line is 0.4cm. Write its length as a fraction of a centimetre.

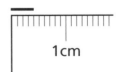

____$\frac{4}{10}$____ cm   1cm

1 mark

19 A hosepipe pours $\frac{1}{5}$ litre of water every second.

How many litres will it pour in 60 seconds? ____12____ l

1 mark

20 How many centimetres less than 1 metre is seven-tenths of a metre? ____30____ cm

1 mark

Total

20 marks

Final test

Section 1

1 What fraction of the whole shape is purple? $\frac{9}{10}$

1 mark

2 Write the next two numbers in the sequence.

$5\frac{4}{10}$, $5\frac{5}{10}$, $5\frac{6}{10}$, $5\frac{7}{10}$, $5\frac{8}{10}$, ___$5\frac{9}{10}$___ , ___6___

1 mark

3 Three pizzas are equally shared between 10 people.

What fraction of a pizza does each get? $\frac{3}{10}$

1 mark

4 $7\text{kg} \div 10 = \dfrac{7}{10}\,\text{kg}$

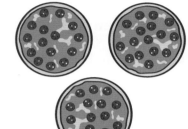

1 mark

Section 2

5 What fraction of these pencil sharpeners are white? $\frac{1}{5}$

1 mark

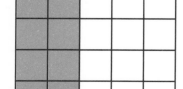

6 What fraction of the cubes are purple? $\frac{5}{6}$ or $\frac{20}{24}$

1 mark

7 What is one-quarter of 8 peanuts? ___2___

1 mark

8 Colour $\frac{2}{5}$ of the 20 squares in this grid.

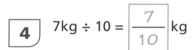
1 mark

Section 3

9 This ruler shows tenths of a centimetre. Mark $\frac{7}{10}$ cm with a cross and $1\frac{1}{10}$ cm with an arrow on this ruler.

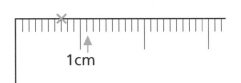

1cm

1 mark

10 What number is the arrow showing?

$7\frac{3}{4}$

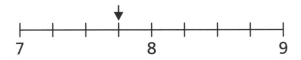

7   8   9

1 mark

11 What fraction is the answer to 1 ÷ 5? $\frac{1}{5}$

1 mark

12 Mark the number $2\frac{2}{3}$ on this line with a cross.

0   1   2   3

1 mark

Section 4

13 One-quarter is how many eighths?

___2___ eighths

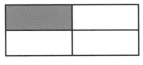

1 mark

14 $\dfrac{2}{3}$ is equivalent to $\dfrac{6}{9}$.

1 mark

15 Circle the fractions that are equivalent to one-half.

$\frac{2}{3}$ $\left(\frac{5}{10}\right)$ $\left(\frac{3}{6}\right)$ $\frac{4}{4}$ $\frac{4}{6}$ $\left(\frac{6}{12}\right)$

1 mark

16 $\dfrac{3}{15} = \dfrac{1}{5}$

1 mark

please turn over

Section 5

17 What is two-sevenths more than three-sevenths? ___$\frac{5}{7}$___

☐ 1 mark

18 Decrease two-thirds by one-third. ___$\frac{1}{3}$___

☐ 1 mark

19 $\frac{1}{8} + \frac{1}{8} + \frac{5}{8} = \boxed{\dfrac{7}{8}}$

☐ 1 mark

20 $\frac{11}{12} - \frac{4}{12} = \boxed{\dfrac{7}{12}}$

☐ 1 mark

Section 6

21 Is one-sixth of a kilogram more or less than one-quarter of a kilogram? ___less___

☐ 1 mark

1kg

22 Tick to show how the fractions in this sequence are ordered:

$\frac{1}{6} \quad \frac{1}{5} \quad \frac{1}{4} \quad \frac{1}{3} \quad \frac{1}{2}$

smallest to largest ✓

largest to smallest ☐

☐ 1 mark

23 Use either the < or > sign to show which is larger.

$\frac{5}{7}$ ⟩ $\frac{3}{7}$

☐ 1 mark

24 Write these fractions from smallest to largest:

$\frac{4}{10} \quad \frac{2}{10} \quad \frac{5}{10} \quad \frac{3}{10}$ ___$\frac{2}{10}$___   ___$\frac{3}{10}$___   ___$\frac{4}{10}$___   ___$\frac{5}{10}$___

☐ 1 mark

Section 7

25 10 bricks weigh 9kg in total. What does one brick weigh?

Give your answer as a fraction of a kilogram. $\dfrac{9}{10}$ kg

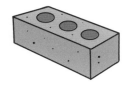

1 mark

26 A bag contains 2 red apples, 6 yellow apples and some green apples. There are 16 apples in the bag.

What fraction of the apples are green? $\dfrac{8}{16}$ or $\dfrac{1}{2}$

1 mark

27 A tart was cut into 9 equal slices.

Leo ate $\dfrac{4}{9}$ of it and James ate the rest.

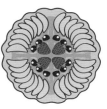

a) Who ate more? _____ James _____

b) How much more did he eat as a fraction of the whole pie? $\dfrac{1}{9}$

1 mark

28 Jo swam a race in $8\dfrac{1}{2}$ seconds.

Molly took three-tenths of a second longer.

How long did Molly take? $8\dfrac{8}{10}$ sec

1 mark

End of test

Total

28 marks

93

Pupil progress chart

Pupil's name _____   Class / set _____

Unit	Get started	Now try these	Challenge	Total
1	/ 8	/ 8	/ 8	/ 24
2	/ 8	/ 8	/ 8	/ 24
3	/ 8	/ 8	/ 8	/ 24
4	/ 8	/ 8	/ 8	/ 24
5	/ 8	/ 8	/ 8	/ 24
6	/ 8	/ 8	/ 8	/ 24
Check-up test 1			/	/ 20
7	/ 8	/ 8	/ 8	/ 24
8	/ 8	/ 8	/ 8	/ 24
9	/ 8	/ 8	/ 8	/ 24
10	/ 8	/ 8	/ 8	/ 24
11	/ 8	/ 8	/ 8	/ 24
12	/ 8	/ 8	/ 8	/ 24
Check-up test 2			/	/ 20
13	/ 8	/ 8	/ 8	/ 24
14	/ 8	/ 8	/ 8	/ 24
15	/ 8	/ 8	/ 8	/ 24
16	/ 8	/ 8	/ 8	/ 24
17	/ 8	/ 8	/ 8	/ 24
18	/ 8	/ 8	/ 8	/ 24
Check-up test 3			/	/ 20

Final test group record sheet

Pupil's name	Y3/F1				Y3/F2				Y3/F3				Y3/F4				Y3/F5				Y3/F6				Y3/F7				Total
	1	2	3	4	5	6	7	8	9	10	11	12	13	14	15	16	17	18	19	20	21	22	23	24	25	26	27	28	
																													/28
																													/28
																													/28
																													/28
																													/28
																													/28
																													/28
																													/28
																													/28
																													/28
																													/28
																													/28
																													/28
																													/28
																													/28
																													/28
																													/28
																													/28
																													/28
																													/28
																													/28
																													/28
																													/28
																													/28
																													/28

Full list of books in the Fractions, Decimals and Percentages series

Pupil books

Fractions 1	ISBN 978 0 7217 1375 5
Fractions 2	ISBN 978 0 7217 1377 9
Fractions 3	ISBN 978 0 7217 1379 3
Fractions 4	ISBN 978 0 7217 1381 6
Fractions 5	ISBN 978 0 7217 1383 0
Fractions 6	ISBN 978 0 7217 1385 4

Teacher's guides

Fractions 1 Teacher's Guide	ISBN 978 0 7217 1376 2
Fractions 2 Teacher's Guide	ISBN 978 0 7217 1378 6
Fractions 3 Teacher's Guide	ISBN 978 0 7217 1380 9
Fractions 4 Teacher's Guide	ISBN 978 0 7217 1382 3
Fractions 5 Teacher's Guide	ISBN 978 0 7217 1384 7
Fractions 6 Teacher's Guide	ISBN 978 0 7217 1386 1

Free downloads available from the Schofield & Sims website

A selection of free downloads is available from the Schofield & Sims website (www.schofieldandsims.co.uk/free-downloads). These may be used to further enhance the effectiveness of the programme. The downloads add to the range of print materials supplied in the teacher's guides.

- **Graphics** slides containing the visual elements from each teacher's guide unit provided as Microsoft PowerPoint® presentations.
- **Go deeper investigations** providing additional extension material to develop problem-solving and reasoning skills.
- **Additional resources** including a fraction wall, a comparison chart and number lines to support learning and teaching.